A CAIRN OF SMALL STONES

ALSO BY JOHN WATTS

Moidart: Among the Clanranalds
Rev. C. MacDonald, 1889, edited J. Watts · 1997

Scalan: The Forbidden College 1716–1799 · 1999

Hugh MacDonald: Highlander, Jacobite and Bishop · 2002

A Canticle of Love: The Story of the Franciscan Sisters of the Immaculate Conception · 2006

John Watts

A CAIRN
of SMALL
STONES

*Being the Recollections of his life, told by Ian
More McLellan of Brinacory to Mr Reginald
McDonell, Priest of North Morar, & done into
English by him out of the Erse Language*

1794

MUNGO

Glasgow

Mungo Books
an imprint of Ovada Books
St Mungo's Retreat, 52 Parson Street, Glasgow, G4 0RX
Tel./Fax: +44 (0)141 552 5523
www.ovadabooks.com   info@ovadabooks.com

ISBN 1-905965-00-1
A Catalogue record for this book is available from the British Library.

Printed in Glasgow by Bell & Bain Ltd.
www.bell-bain.co.uk

For Moira

Contents

Acknowledgements

The author wishes to thank the staff of the National Library of Scotland, the Scottish National Archives, the libraries of the Society of Antiquaries of Scotland and of Gillis College, and the Scottish Catholic Archives, as well as the Special Collections Department and a number of the specialist libraries of the University of Edinburgh. In particular I acknowledge the help of Professor Michael Lynch and Mrs Williamson of the Department of Scottish History at the University. The former was kind enough to read the text in draft as were Mr Alasdair Roberts, Mrs Nancy Clusker, Stephen and Eleanor Watts, and the late Abbot Mark Dilworth, and a number of their suggestions have been included in the final version.

Introduction

The story told in this book is set in the eighteenth century in Morar in the West Highlands of Scotland. The visitor to the area today would find it hard to imagine its remoteness three hundred years ago. The Highlands were still isolated from the rest of Scotland by distance, language, and a complete absence of roads, and the few travellers from the South who ventured beyond the Highland Line spoke of the experience as if they were 'surveying a sort of New World'.[1] Even after a sparse network of roads had been built by General Wade as lines of communication for the British army after the '15, visitors rarely strayed far from them, and when Thomas Pennant made his Highland tour in 1769 he was travelling through what was still 'an almost undescribed country'.[2]

The areas bordering on the sea in the West, which included Morar as well as Moidart, Arisaig, and Knoydart, were among the most impenetrable. Known collectively as 'the Rough Bounds', they were commonly called even by their neighbours 'the Highlands of the Highlands' and travellers were advised against attempting to the enter them. 'Almost from the commencement of our journey', one wrote to Walter Scott as late as 1800, 'we had been instructed to consider the Rough Bounds as impassable.'[3]

To the local people at this time Morar was not one country but two, with the loch, river and estuary the boundary separating them. The one, South Morar, comprised the main part of the lands of MacDonald of Morar; the other, North Morar, belonged to MacDonell of Glengarry.

It is the latter that is the setting for the present story. Lying between the fresh water loch that bears its name and the salt water of Loch Nevis, it formed with Knoydart the western extreme of Glengarry country. It lay far over the mountains from the seat of the Chief, who thought of it as a 'wild and excentrick' part of his lands.[4] In 1768 he sold it to General Simon Fraser to pay off his debts, and it became and remained until very recently a part of the Lovat estate.

Wild it may have been, but not uninhabited. Whereas today its population is almost wholly confined to its western end, in and around the fishing port of Mallaig and the village of Morar, in those days there was neither village nor port and the settlements were fairly evenly distributed from the coast eastwards to the heads of the two lochs. Most of the bays and river mouths sustained a 'farm town' of several tenant families, who divided whatever there was of cultivable land for planting oats and bere, brought their cattle up to the shielings in the summer, and shared the great tracts of rough hill grazing for their sheep and horses.

North Morar and the other districts of the Rough Bounds were almost entirely Catholic at this time.

With certain islands in the west and a few glens in the eastern Highlands and seaboard, they had retained the Old Faith – now virtually extinct elsewhere in Scotland – through their isolation, the leadership of their chiefs and tacksmen, and the labours of their priests.[5] This gave them a certain embattled sense of common cause, and further isolated them from the rest of the country, which was inclined to think of them – if it was aware of them at all – as wedded to error and no doubt in league with foreign powers. In the eyes of the Establishment they were doubly suspect, their support for the exiled House of Stuart and their loyalty to Rome but two sides of the one coin of disaffection.

Though isolated they did enjoy some contact with outside society. Cattle drovers came in and out; tinkers travelled through, selling their hand-made wares; and a few local people sought seasonal work elsewhere. In the '15 and the '45 many travelled with the Jacobite armies and had their eyes opened to the wider world. In the second half of the century Clyde fishing fleets came north to the coastal lochs for the herring season, and provided casual work for local men and women.[6] And in the thirty years before the century's end hundreds of families emigrated to America, or else to the towns of the Lowlands, and sent back word of their new way of life there.

Gradually, also, the Highlands were beginning to feel the impact of the agricultural improvement that had been introduced from England and adopted first in the more fertile soils of the Lowlands. In time the old runrig system of tillage gave way to a more rational division of the land, more efficient methods of production were adopted, and the ancient breeds of kyloe cattle, small hardy horses and short-tailed sheep began to be replaced by new breeds brought in from the South.[7] These changes occurred most slowly in the remote and conservative North and West, particularly perhaps in places like the Rough Bounds where Jacobite chiefs and tenantry were instinctively resistant to anything that originated in the lands of their enemies.[8] Even there, though, they were beginning to be felt well before the century came to a close.

After the '45 the Government brought in legislation aimed at destroying the power of the Highland chiefs and the people's dependence upon them. Backed up by a ruthless military presence, in time it successfully and finally dismantled the traditional clan system, and so played a vital part in changing for ever the old way of life of the Highlands. When Dr Johnson made his tour in 1773 he discovered that he had arrived too late to find what he was hoping to see. 'There was perhaps never any change of national manners so quick, so great, and so general as that which has operated in the Highlands by the last conquest and the subsequent laws', he wrote.[9]

As the chiefs lost their judicial authority over their people and their need for them in battle, so the relationship between them changed from one of interdependence to one of economic pragmatism. Many chiefs began to raise rents while at the same time dividing the land among an ever greater number of tenants, as the Highland population rose in the second half of the century.

Their drive for wealth at the expense of the people not only prompted massive emigration but dealt a blow to the old blood loyalties and, in the words of a contemporary Highlander, 'unhinged the social virtues' that had stood for generations.[10] It is for such reasons that the eighteenth century has been called the period in the Highlands when medievalism and modernism touched.[11] But still at its end something remained of the old. 'The feudal system has been abolished', wrote one of the great landowners as the new century opened, 'but the customs that arose out of it are not forgotten. An act of parliament, supported by a military force, could destroy the one; only time can eradicate the other.'[12] Probably as much of the old survived in North Morar as anywhere on the mainland of Scotland.

By the mid-eighteenth century the Church of Scotland had a well established parish structure throughout the Highlands, with Gaelic speaking ministers supported in their work by catechists and schools.[13] But its failure to make real inroads into the Catholic areas was a constant source of frustration. 'Where so little good seed of any kind is sown,' wrote the authors of a Church-commissioned report of 1760, 'is it to be wondered at that the enemy shoud sow his tares and that these shoud bring forth a plentiful increase?'[14] The General Assembly appealed to the Crown to set up more parishes in the Rough Bounds and the Catholic islands, and even recommended that 'colonies' of Protestants be settled there.[15] Small-scale colonisation was in fact attempted on several of the Forfeited Estates. But in North Morar, despite repeated pleas, no minister, missionary church or school was established.[16]

For much of the century the Catholic Church was hampered by a grave shortage of priests to serve the people, and the few that it had suffered a constant struggle against poverty, illness and an impossible burden of work. Even fewer were the native Highland priests who could speak the language of the people, and it was one of the priorities of Hugh MacDonald, son of the Laird of Morar, when appointed the first bishop of the Highlands in 1731, to remedy this.[17] But he was hampered by lack of funds, and by factionalism within the ranks of the clergy that threatened to undermine his authority. The latter was only brought to a halt by the Rising of 1745, which overtook it but whose aftermath itself did incalculable damage to the standing of the Church.

These were troubles the Catholic people of the Highlands and Islands could have done without, living as they were under the Penal Laws, according to which they already stood to suffer imprisonment, loss of inheritance and even banishment for the practice of their faith.[18] Yet their steadfast piety even in the hardest times was attested by all.[19]

They enjoyed some good years among the bad. Because of their remoteness and poverty they were sometimes left fairly well alone, and the priests were able to go about their work with some impunity, carrying their vestments with them and often celebrating the Mass outdoors, to the chagrin of their enemies. Only at certain times, notably at the beginning of the century and again after the '15 and the '45, were the laws enforced rigorously, with a heavy military presence and much suffering, before life gradually returned to 'normal' once more.[20] By the late 1770s, when it had become clear that the Jacobite threat had evaporated, Catholics were beginning to enjoy a degree of religious liberty unknown for two hundred years. And with the passing of the Scottish Catholic Relief Act of 1793 their new freedom was finally recognised in law.

The picture we have of North Morar at this time is restricted by the paucity of contemporary sources. Being remote, disaffected and Catholic, it was rarely visited by the kirk ministers and other officials who have left such valuable accounts of other parts of the North West. There are no baptismal records, for there was good reason why none should be kept. Nor do we have the factors' reports and contemporary maps that are available for many of the Forfeited Estates. Some cursory and sporadic details of

land use, fishing and rentals, and lists of principal
tenants are extant, as are first-hand sources concerning the emigrations of the '80s and '90s.[21] And
among the wealth of contemporary correspondance
held in the Scottish Catholic Archives are a number
of letters that pertain to North Morar.[22] Finally, we
have the indirect evidence of the extensive primary
sources that exist for adjacent areas of the Highlands where the way of life was similar.[23]

A Cairn of Small Stones is the life story of one local
man, Ian More McLellan, a tenant of the farm of
Brinacory, as told in his native Gaelic to the priest
of North Morar in 1793 and set down by him in the
English language. Ian was nearly ninety at the time
of the telling, having lived nearly all his years in his
native farm town. His story thus spans almost the
whole of the eighteenth century, and the greater
part of it is set in one small and isolated place. But
(as we saw) it was a place touched from time to
time by the events of the outside world, and whose
own way of life changed with the passing years. So
his account presents a detailed close-up of a narrow
world, but with glimpses of a wider horizon and
greater happenings farther afield.

The man to whom he related it, Fr Ranald Mac-
Donell, had arrived in North Morar in 1782. He
was to remain in the same station for fifty-eight
years altogether, a MacDonell among MacDonells,

until his death in 1840. He was one of that heroic breed of priests who devoted their whole lives to serving a poor, remote, unheard-of people. Ian's story, faithfully translated, reflects his perceptions and insights and the strengths and limitations of his outlook on the world. In it he thinks and speaks as a man of his time and place. Only in his brief experience of schooling as a boy was he atypical, for a Highlander of his condition would not normally have received any education. It gave him an understanding of basic English that often proved useful in later life. He would have been one of only a handful in North Morar at the time with any English at all.

Like most of his neighbours he was a Jacobite. With them, also, he shared the piety and deep religious sense of the culture into which he was born, and it is not by chance that the first word of his story, and its last is 'God'. The reader should not look for the insights of modern psychology, or socioeconomic analysis, or 'Romantic' descriptions of landscape among his memories, for they contain none of these. But they often draw upon the wisdom and the beauties of oral poetry, and proverbial truth. His métier was the centuries-old tradition of story-telling to which he was heir.

At the time when his memories were set down the spelling of English was already close to the modern, but not fully standardised. Thus, not only did his translator use a few archaic spellings but he was not always consistent in his use of them. When writing

the names of people and places which are angli-
cisations of the original Gaelic he used the style
of anglicisation current at the time. In the case of
most personal forenames this involved an equivalent based on the baptismal Latin – 'Reginald' for
his own name Raonull ('Ranald'), 'Aeneas' for
'Aonghas' ('Angus'), and so on. Other names were
generally written in a form further from the Gaelic
than we normally use today: the story teller styled
himself 'Ian More McLellan', rather than the modern 'Iain Mór MacLellan', for example. Priests were
entitled 'Mr' not 'Fr', this being originally a reference to their Master's degree and the equivalent of
the title 'Maighstir' still used for them in Gaelic
speech today.

In the case of place names, forms such as 'Srone
Gower', 'Skerry Glass', etc., were simply the
attempts of English-speaking clerks and cartogra-
phers to approximate to the Gaelic sound. Most
should be easily recognisable as they occur in the
text, and reference to the comparative map on p.
xxv will allow them to be readily located.

Ian used the old Scottish values for distance, capac-
ity and money, and these the translator retained:
the Act of Union may have begun the process of
standardisation in theory, but in practice the traditional and local methods of calculation often per-
sisted, especially in the Highlands and among the
older generation.

Finally, I have included a number of brief notes
to clarify or amplify the text for today's reader, but

these have been kept to a minimum and placed at the end of the book, with page references, so as not to intrude upon the story.

A Cairn of Small Stones is presented in the hope that those who read it may take pleasure from it, as well as gaining some insight into a way of life long gone. If they visit Brinacory today they will find no-one living there − only the barely discernible marks of old lazybeds, the ruins of a few stone 'white houses', and a small school abandoned years ago. Walking on to Swordland they will encounter only a lodge, lived in for a few weeks of the year by outsiders. And at Tarbert they will come upon one old man living alone, one of the dwindling number of native Gaelic speakers of the old tradition left in North Morar.

1. The phrase is from a letter of Rev. J Walker to Lord
    Kaimes, 1764, following his fact-finding visit to the
    Highlands and Islands; MS La iii 352/1, Edinburgh
    Univ. Library.

2. J. Knox *A Tour through the Highlands of Scotland and
    the Hebride Islands in MDCCLXXIV* (London, 1787), p.
    lxi, describing the journey of his predecessor Thomas
    Pennant.

3. Letter to Walter Scott, 23 August 1800, in J. Leyden
    *Journal of a Tour in the Highlands and Western Islands of
    Scotland in* 1800, ed. J. Simon (Edinburgh and London,
    1903).

4. Gordon Castle Muniments, Reports on various parts
    of the estate – Morhir (1768), GD 44/25/28, NAS.

5. For details of the Catholic areas see O. Blundell *The
    Catholic Highlands of Scotland*, 2 vols. (Sands & Co.,
    1909–1917). In the West they mainly comprised the
    lands of Clanranald, Morar, Glengarry and MacNeil
    of Barra; most of those in the East lay within the es-
    tates of the Duke of Gordon.

6. On 18th c. droving see A. R. B. Haldane *The Drove
    Roads of Scotland* (1952; rev. edn. 1973). Contempo-
    rary accounts of the fishing in the west coast sea lochs
    include J. Knox *Observations on the Northern Fisheries*
    (London, 1786), and J. Anderson *An Account of the
    Present State of the Hebrides and Western Coasts of Scotland*
    (Edinburgh, 1785). For a detailed modern account see
    the earlier chapters of J. Dunlop *The British Fisheries
    Society* 1786–1893 (Edinburgh, 1978).

7. Still the most useful general summary of the changes

is in M. Gray *The Highland Economy 1750–1850* (Edinburgh, 1957). Specific to North Morar is D. Turnock, 'North Morar – the Improving Movement on a West Highland Estate', *Scot. Geog. Mag.*, 85, (April 1969).

8. Ironically, some of the most fiercely Jacobite estates, having been most active in the Rising of 1745, were annexed by the Crown after its defeat, and so were the first to experience the new methods of farming and other 'civilising' developments in housing, conditions of tenure, and education. One such was the Barrisdale estate in Knoydart, across the loch from North Morar. Cf., R.W. Munro *Taming the Rough Bounds: Knoydart 1745–1784*, Soc. of West Highland & Island Historical Research (Coll 1984).

9. S. Johnson *Journey to the Western Islands* (1775, 1926 ed.), 76.

10. Maj. Gen. D. Stewart *Sketches of the Character, Institutions and Customs of the Highlands of Scotland* (1822; Inverness, 1885), 270.

11. I. F. Grant *Everyday Life in an old Highland Farm 1769–1782* (London, 1924; rev. edn. 1981), 2.

12. T. Douglas, Earl of Selkirk *Observations on the Present State of the Highlands of Scotland* (London, 1805), 10.

13. The schools were financed either by the parishes or by the Society in Scotland for the Propagation of Christian Knowledge. From 1725 the Kirk's provision of ministers, catechists and teachers benefited from grants from the King's Bounty. For a good general account of these developments see J. MacInnes *The Evangelical Movement in the Highlands of Scotland 1688–1800* (Aberdeen, 1951).

14. Report of Drs Hyndman, Dick et al, to the General Assembly (1760), CH 8/212, NAS. The Kirk's frustrations, problems and solutions are well described in Ferguson, W. 'The Problems of the Established Church in the West Highlands and Islands in the Eighteenth Century', *RSCHS*, xvii (1969).

15. General Assembly Papers (1727), CH 1/5/51, p. 187, NAS.

16. The requests were made by the Synod of Glenelg, within whose boundaries North Morar lay – cf., the original Minutes of the Synod, CH 2/568, NAS; selections from them also in T.M. Murchison 'The Synod of Glenelg, 1725–1821. Notes from the Records', *TGSI*, 3 (1937–41).

17. Bishop Hugh MacDonald's Report to the Cardinals of Propaganda Fide, 20 March 1732, (in Latin), Blairs Letters, SCA; English translation in A. Bellesheim *History of the Catholic Church of Scotland*, trans. D. O. Hunter Blair (Edinburgh, 1890) vol. iv, Appendix xiii, 389f. For an account of the bishop's work and the problems he faced, see J. Watts *Hugh MacDonald: Highlander, Jacobite and Bishop* (Edinburgh, 2002).

18. No less than twenty-one laws had been passed against them since the Union of Crowns in 1603, culminating in the 'Act for preventing the Grouth of Popery' of 1700 (*APS*, x, 215f – cf., A.I. MacInnes, 'Catholic Recusancy and the Penal Laws, 1603–1707', *RSCHS*, xxiii (1987–9), which gives details of the successive legislation. Further laws were passed in the first three decades of the eighteenth century.

19. One of the most striking accounts was the Report on

the Highland Mission of Fr Alex Leslie in the late 17th c. – Report and Itinerary (English versions, SM 2/9/1 and SM 2/9/3 respectively, SCA). Fr Leslie wrote of the people's 'great piety and insatiable thirst for the sacraments', and their 'fervent zeal', likening them in their simple and rock-like steadfastness to the first Christians.

20. Cf., eg., Bishop John Geddes' Ms. 'Some Account of the State of the Catholic Religion in Scotland During the Years 1745, 1746, 1747', SCA; also printed in W. Forbes Leith *Memoirs of Scottish Catholics During the XVIIth and XVIIIth Centuries* (London, 1909) ii, 336 ff.

21. Regarding the former, see for example – Details and Reports of the Glengarry estate, GD 44/25/23, NAS. Re. the emigrations, see the bibliography of primary sources from both sides of the Atlantic in M. McLean *The People of Glengarry* (Toronto, 1991).

22. In particular the Blairs Letters (BL) and to a lesser extent the Oban Letters (OL). The former includes some correspondence of MacDonald of Morar and other local gentlemen, and numerous letters of clergy, including a number from Bishop Hugh MacDonald and Fr Ranald MacDonell.

23. Notable among printed works are J. Sinclair *General View of the Agriculture of the Northern Counties and Islands of Scotland* (1795); J. Robertson *General View of the Agriculture in the County of Inverness* (1808); and the relevant volumes of *The Statistical Account of Scotland, 1795* ed. J. Sinclair. This in addition to the numerous Ms. sources, and a number of valuable accounts of sojourns in or journeys through the Highlands by contemporary men of letters.

Gazeteer

Alphabetical list of place names from map, with grid references.
Spellings as in map and text, with correct OS map spellings in parentheses
where different.

Airor C7
Ardintigh F4
Ardnamurach G4
Beoraid C4
Beoraidbeg B/C4
Bourblach B4
Bracarina (*Bracorina*) D4
Bracora D4
Brinacory E3
Brinacory Island E3
Brumasaig F5
Carnoch I5
Culnamuck
  (*Cùil a' Mhuic*) G3
Drumcullin
  (*Druim Chuilinn*) F4
Finiscaig (*Finiskaig*) I5
Gewish Island
  (*Eilean Guibhais*) D6
Glasnacardoch B/C5
Glassgile (*Glaschoille*) D6
Glen Dessary J4
Guidale (*Goaideil*) B/C1
Inverbeg (*Inbhir Beag*) E4
Inverie F6
Kiles (*Kyles*) G4
Killichoan (*Kilchoan*) F6

Kilmory B2
Kinloch (*Kinloch Morar*) I3
Letir Morar
  (*Letter Morar*) D3
Lochnankeel
  (*Loch nan Ceall*) A–B 1–2
Mallegveck (*Mallaigvaig*) C5
Mallegvore (*Mallaigmore*) C5
Mewboll (*Meoble*) F2
Middle Island
  (*An t-Eilean Meadhoin*) C4
Oban I3
Red Skerries
  (*Sgeirean Dearga*) D/E6
Romasag (*Romasaig*) C7
Rua Roanell
  (*Rubha Roanaill*) D6
Sandaig Bay D6/7
Skerryglass
  (*Sgeiran Glasa*) E6
Srone Gower
  (*Sròn Ghaothar*) F3
Srone Vore (*Sròn Mhòr*) G3
Swordland F3
Tarbert F4
Trigh (*Traigh*) B3
White Island (*Eilean Bàn*) C4

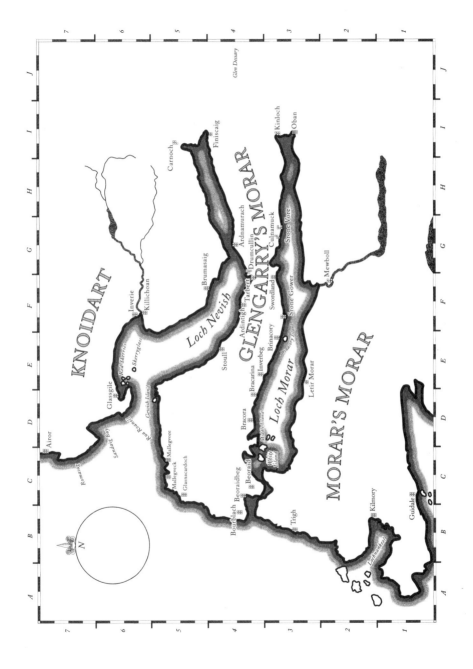

Preface of the Translator

IT was some years ago, a litle after I had first
arrived as priest in North Morar, that I made a
visit to the home of Ian More McLellan – Ian mac
Ian Roy vich Yonill – a tenant of the farm of Brinacory, & we walked upon the hill together. He
was allready past eighty years of age. On our walk
he pointed out to me the rock where Mass was said
in by gone times, and told me of the games he & his
friends had play'd beside it as children. He recalled
the names of all of them, and the details of their
lives, with a sharp & exact memory remarkable for
one so old. And it seem'd to me that it woud be
instructive to record from his own mouth the life
that was led in those days, now that so much of the
old way is vanish'd, and how men followed their
ffaith then, now that (thank God) it is no longer
needfull to keep it secret.

I therefor proposed to him that that he shoud tell
me the events of his own life, and that I woud com-
mit his memorial to paper. When I first put this
idea to him he was loth to agree, and several years
elapsed before it was done. He believed that the
events of lives such as his woud be thoght of litlc
importance & not worthy of being written down.

It is true, ours is a small & distant corner of the
land, and for most of the time we have no more
news here than if we were not in the world. The

publick may therefor, like Ian, question whether a life so humble & remote is fit matter for a narrative.

'Can any thing good thing come out of Morar?' the reader may ask. 'What could be worth recording of the life of one born in a hutt with cattle, one who counted carpenter amoung his trades?'

If so, the reader has provided his own answer. For surely the humblest man is equal to the king, in the eyes of the King of Kings, & it is in the ordinariness of our lives that lies hid the glory of God.

I met Ian on a number of occasions, & he told his tale, beginning at his childhood near the opening of our century and carrying it forward to the present day near to the close of it. At my request he gave descriptions of people, places & happenings, even where these were allready familiar and obvious to my self, because it was allways my hope that his memorials woud be read by others who woud have no knowledge of Highland life nor of our people.

After each meeting I at once set down his narrative in the English language, so that what is written pretty closely follows his own words. My memory may have err'd here and there, & upon occasion I was obliged to alter his phrase where an exact translation could not have rendred the sense without obscurity or awkwardness, but in every other wise I have faithfully followed him.

In order to make a book from his narrative I have arranged it in to chapters, concluding each one at what seem'd a natural place, & I have taken the liberty of giving to each a title.

As to anyone who may read the pages that follow, perhaps his interest in Highland life has already been whetted by the descriptions of Dr Johnson, Mr Pennant and others, lately publish'd. If so, I hope that he will find the chief virtue of the present volume to be that it contains the words not of a traveller from the outside world, but of one whose whole life was lived within the world he tells of.

A cairn may be built of small stones, so the proverb tells us, and it is in this confidence that I present the story of Ian's life among his neighbours in the pages that follow, as fit to stand and endure, and to point the road to us who come after him.

REVD. REGINALD McDONELL
Feast of Pentecost, 1794

I

My earliest memories

GOD be in my remembering, and in the telling of
my story!

My mother was near to dying when she bore me,
and they say I struggled into the world ailing. It
was thought I woud not live more than a day or
two. The people of our farm here at Brinacory
were praying for us to the Virgin mother and to
Brigid. We had no priest of our own at that time,
but Mr Colum the priest of Knoidart was staying
since the Autumn on the White Island near to the
mouth of our loch, & the word was that he was
lodging this night at Bracora.

My father being away it was my mother's mother
who took me up. She wrapt me under her plaid
for my safekeeping in the night and at once sett off
West to find the priest. She was on the road three
hours, scrambling among the rocks with her one
hand free. At one place the path passes over the
shoulder of the hill high above the water so that
to slip you risque falling to your death. Here she
met the sudden force of the wind and rain. Tho'
she managed to avoid the fall she arrived wet to
her skin at the house where the priest was lodging.
There I was baptised. She waited for no more than

1704
Nov^{ber}

one mouthfull of whiskey, and started at once for home with the rain at her back, and set me in my mother's arms as the dawn broke.

But the soaking had done its work, and that day began the feever that killed her. (She told my mother that in the Summer past she had seen a cuckoo on our roof before she had broken her fast, and she knew then that some one was sure to die: she had feared it wou'd be my mother or the child in her womb, but now that our danger was passing she knew that it was herself.) She died when I was four weeks old, may God be mercifull to her. But my mother lived, and I survived too, as you see.

1707   All these things my mother told me. Of my own first memory itself I was not yet three years old at the time of it. I mind standing at our door with my whole family and I peering out from amoung them. It was night and I coud just tell the mountains from the sky. We were watching a dozen glowing red Lights moving in a line down the hill. Very slow they moved, some times twisting, some times hid, some times glowing yellow, some times they seemed to have stopt. At last they came down and right into our farm.

My father told us that it was Bishop James, coming from far beyond the hills in the East. He was bound for the White Island. When ever he came to a farm on his journey the men of that farm would guide him to the next one untill he safely reached the end of his road. These were the men of Swordland and the lights they carried were glowing peats on sticks, which the wind on the hill can not put out but only makes them glow brighter.

I mind the crowd & the talking & the drink. Bishop James had a priest of the Highlands with him to speak for him, since he had nothing of our language but only Latin & English. I recall kissing his hand, but I have no memory of his face. And then we watched that same line of lights returning in to the East, and a second line – this was our men, and my father among them – winding away slowly over in to the West.

All the night times in our house have become a single memory – it is more than eighty years past, after all! My father is beside the fire, drinking from the wooden cup with the writing carved on it that he boght from a sailor. My mother sits facing him. Smoak hangs under the roof beams. There are a bunch of fir splinters stuck in to the pot chain over the fire, and a couple of lighted ones fixed in the wall. The floor has been swept for the night, the wattle door is pulled shut, and a turf set in the window. My brothers and my sister & I are sat around the fire. The corners of the house are in darkness, It is the time for stories and songs.

This is when we learned about the generations of our family. Our mother told us of when she lost her third child, six years before I was born, after three harvests failed in Glengarry's Morar. Catherine, another woman of our farm, saved her two boys that year only by suckling them herself (hav-

ing lost her youngest), and they allready five and
seven years old.

Other nights our parents woud tell us of the old
Heroes, and sing the songs that the women sang at
their work and that we had learnt on the knee –

Would that I were strong and knowing,
That Cu Chulainn's strength were in my blows.

And it was the greatest ambition of Donald and
Calum and myself to grow to the strength of a man
like him, or like McAllan's Son who they say was
the strongest man who ever lived in Morar.

Most nights we had neighbors in and out, for
as my father woud say, 'A man, be he friend or
stranger, is allways welcome thorow our door, even
tho' he had an other man's head under his arm'. Yet
the chief memory that I hold is of our family alone,
with peat ash on the floor, and our father taking his
snuff, and myself fighting to stay awake to hear the
talk, but falling asleep anyway on the bed of heathers spred upon the floor at the house end.

When we slept our parents' work was not yet over,
for the evenings were allways a time of making,
whether Winter or Summer. I mind once waking,
and thinking it might be nearly morning. One fir
candle was burning still. All were sleeping save my
mother, and she was kneeling at the fire to smother
it. I watched her gather the embers in to the shape
of a Targe, and put three peats amoung them in the
name of the Blessed Trinity, and carefully cover

them with enough white ash. I watched her pray to Christ and His mother and our Guardian Angel of the door, before she too lay down. Beyond that door I cou'd hear the trees roaring in the wind, but in side not a flicker of the candle.

In my boy's memory it was allways long days of sun shine at our farm, and the loch and meadows and rocks sparkling, and every tree in leaf – 'willow of the brook, hazel of the rock, alder of the bog, birch of the hollow, and ash of the sunny slope', as the proverb says. In the Spring you would find me at the cattle with Calum, for the beasts who had fill'd their bellies on the Infield in the Winter must now be kept away from it, & this was the job for myself and Calum with our wands. Some days we woud drive them up in to the Outfield, and there herd them in to a different place every new week, so that the whole field woud be well manured. The Infield was manured mostly with dung of the house, but this was work only for our father and the other men, who woud lift it from the house ends to scatter after the digging. They used to sow one year of bere, and two of oats.

As the days grew longer it was our job to find herbs for the house. Some were for use against illness, and others for dyes for the fleeces. As soon as good leaves were on the Birch and the bog mirtle we woud gather them, and in June we looked for the flowering broom, for all these gave a yellow dye. At the same season we could find the Sorrell, but it grew only in dryer soil and gave a red, the

1711

same colour as its flowers. The docking plant was the easiest – it grows every where and we could dig for it at any time, and its roots gave my mother her black. Blue was allways the last dye she made, because the Blaeberry is not ripe untill late Summer. For her brown she could use tree bark, but she woud rather have Dulse from the rock. And for this we had to walk with our creels up over the hill to Ardintigh – it is three good miles – and there it grows in plenty by the low tide. Some women chuse other plants for their colours, but these were the ones our mother believed in.

She allso used to keep the dulse for our sore stomacks and sore heads and whensoever one of us had worms, which was pretty often, she would make a drink of it. But she said that to work well it must be drunk fasting untill noon, and she used to keep us within doors all morning to be sure we woud not get our teeth into food.

When the longest day was near we awaited the first settled weather for the cutting of the peats. All from the farm worked together then, and there was work for the children too. From twelve we boys were allow'd below with the men to take a share of cutting and throwing them up. The younger ones must remain at the top where they helped the women stack. When once you got cutting you considered your self a man.

In the late Summer it was our task to make wicks for the house lamp. Best for this were the rushes that grew in the wet hollow below Archina's house.

We had to split the stems and peel the skin almost away, leaving the pith which made a fine long wick, so long as we worked slowly. By late Summer the pith was firm but not quite dried out. We woud make dozens of them for the long nights. I once made one the length of my fore-arm.

In those days we mainly took as our food Oatmeal and milk. When we rose our mother sett before us meal boiled. For the mid-day she prepared bannocks, which we ate with milk. At the mouth of the night we finished the morn's meal. There were no potatos in our country then, tho' now there is seldom a day but they are eaten. I had grandchildren of my own before I ever saw or tasted one. When meal grew scarce at the end of Winter, our mother mingled husks in it to spin it out, the longer the scarcity the more the husks in it. Nearly every Spring, even after a good harvest, the time came when our grain expired entirely and we must buy from out side our own country – usually it was the men of Sky who provided it.

It is true that there was little bread and many round it in our home at this time, but as our mother would say, 'Better the little bannock with a blessing than the big one with a curse', and 'Many the poor man with husks in his bowl all year round'.
We boys caught a fish or two in the loch, and some times in the Autumn our father broght back herring which we dried and hung under the roof. Alltogether I think we had more than we have today when there are so many mouths on so little land.

I was any way the lucky one for I was the last of the chickens to hatch and it was allways I who got the small bannock made with the last of the meal left over at a cooking. My mother woud make a hole in the middle of it with her thumb, and this was lucky. I think she favored me also because I was delicat from my birth. Whensoever there was goat's or mare's milk in place of cow's, it was mine. Thanks to her I am here today. But there was a price to pay too, for I mind her often enough boiling dandelions, root and leaf, and forcing me to swallow the bitter drink – 'It will stop the bannocks from jumping back out and rolling away', she used to say, and this I could not understand, for had not my teeth allready ground them into fragments?

1713 When I was about eight my stomack had become so weak, in any case, and my chest so weakened by frequent coughing – for all her dandelions – that it was decided my father shoud take me over in to Knoidart to a Chirurgeon who lived amongst those people and who was at that time visited by the sick from far and wide. Aeneas Beaton was his name; he was the last of that name to follow Medicine in the country of Glengarry, and the last Phisician to have received his art in the old way, pass'd by word of mouth and from father to son. Since his time any doctor we have seen here has gained his knowledge in the Colleges of the Low Country.

This man lett some of my blood, but I do not recall if he did any thing else to me. Nor do I mind if he cured me. But I thank God for our meeting any way, for it was in his house that I first cast my eyes upon a book. (I had seen the priest's Missal before, right enough, and I thought that was the only kind of book that existed.) Aeneas had a good few lying by his bed, and he told me that they contained the words of antient men of Medicine from far countries, some written in Latin & others in our own tongue. My eye at once fell upon the smallest, and he permitted me to take it in my hand. Its covering was of red hide, and as I turned over the pages of it I came upon figures of parts of men's bodies, and of stars. I think it was from that day that first grew my respect for learning.

You can be sure that it was more than oat meal we ate whensoever there was a marriage at any of the farms, or at the time of a baptism. And be sure it was more than milk we drank, man or child. And the same or better at Easter & Christmas and the feast of St Michael. On these days the Mass was said at the Stone at Tarbert, so that the people could reach it from both lochs. I mind our family arriving early one Michael's Day, and I climbing the hill above the Stone to watch the people coming. We had the wind strong from the West, as we often have about that time of the year, and sunshine and shadow chasing one another over the land. I coud see the people walking on the hill and in the glen below me, like countless deer coming down to the water, & they were all faced towards the Stone. There were those allmost too young to walk, & those allmost too old. It seemed as if the whole world was on the move, and I never guess'd untill that day that so many could be living in our Countrey. That picture has allways stay'd in my mind since, & every year after, whiles I was a boy, I woud make sure to get there early and climb upon the hill to watch them.

After the Mass the men allways held a race from the water's edge of our loch to the strand of Loch Nevish. The champion at that time was a tennant of the farm of Ardnamurach; he was a full cousin of our father and he won the race every year of my memory. The children and the women woud gather by the winning place to watch the men come over, and once they were all finished a race was held after for the boys round the bay.

There were other stones for Mass in our country – one in the farm of Bracora and one at Beoraidbeg at the mouth of the loch. Whiles we had a priest of our own the Mass woud be said at one of these places every Sunday, Winter or Summer, if ever the weather was fair. But in the years when we had to share the priest from Knoidart or Morar's Morar it might be months we woud be without Mass, except we could take a boat across.

There is a rock up under the hill by the Outfield of our own farm that they say was once used for the Mass, but it never was in my life time. The stream beside it is called The Priest's Burn yet; it was from there that he took his water. Often we play'd near that place, but never did boy or girl climb upon that rock or touch it.

There was an other place we staid clear of allso. This was the little bay that faces over to Letir Morar, but we called it The Bay of Drowning, for it was said that a woman was once made to drown there, upon the word of Glengarry, for some crime she had done. She was tied to the rocks at the water's edge, so that the storm waves woud cover her. Often we talked of what her crime might be, and we never ventured near the bay without a thrill of fear. We used to stand upon the bank above, & watch to see would any bird perch or sing in the Rowan that stood beside the shingle, but none ever did, whether for her crime or for the killing of her.

From a young boy I had watched my father or our neighbors whiles they made creels for the peat, & I learned from them which wands of willow or hazel to chuse, and how to weave and tie them. And when I was nine and my father was for building a new currach he judged that I knew enough to help him at the work. He had kept an entire cow's hide from the Winter for the purpose, and we had been gathering willow wands for weeks – you need more than a hundred and each must be cut long enough for the job. Our mother and Michaelina had been twisting the binding string from horse hair thorow many a light evening. The making it self took us three days and at the end of it we had a fine craft, sturdy & tight, the same hight as my self when we stood it on its rim. It was perfect for the sheltered bays, or even to cross the loch in fair

1714

weather. And my father said that since I had helped to build it, I might share it.

My best friend at that time was Donald, Brinacory's son. He was a year older than me. His mother had died in child birth when he was seven, and my parents had taken him into our home – it was a common thing in those days for a Gentleman's son to be foster'd by a Neighbour of his farm. He had stayed with us for nearly three years, and by this date he was back in his own house a year. He had the use of his father's currach allso, and so the first fine day we had we were for testing mine on the loch. The day broke dead calm, and we set out early, I with my dog ffriend curled up at my feet. By mid day we had worked our way right up to Kinloch and there we staid for a good few hours. And that was our mistake, for whiles we play'd a breeze was rising from the West, and the sun was moving out over the sea. When at last we sett out for home it was allready late, and the sun was off all but the tops of the hills. I did not know it yet but this was to be the worst night of my young life.

The current running up the loch was holding us back. We were not yet past Culnamuck and the wind was now stronger and full in to our faces. We were going backwards in stead of forewards! Nor if we came to shore cou'd we progress on foot, for just there the rocks were too steep and close to the water. There was nothing to be done but camp and wait for the wind. We had our plaids to wrap our selves in, right enough, & the currachs to curl up under.

We chose a little sandy spot as near to the water's edge as possible, with a scrap of meadow at our back. We were glad that we had ffriend. Donald had seen a single hind up on the hill, which he said was a sign that the fairies might he near. We stood looking to the West and the shadows of the hills, & watching for any sign of the wind dropping. But it was not for dropping. We made our 'beds' close together beneath our currachs, with ffriend betwixt us. We plan'd to talk away the time but, weary with all our work, we soon slept,

I awoke with a stiff neck, and peept out. The moon was up & dancing on the wavelets. The wind had dropt all right. I threw off my shell to look about. A sudden chill breeze swept from the West over the water & I sensed that the Silent People were in our company. I blessed my self and reached for ffriend. But he was staring at the meadow behind us, and his neck bristling. I looked where he was looking. At the far side of the dell beside the rocks stood a huge dog. Now I was certain there were spirits here. Was this the gost-dog they say walks in Mewboll, in the country of McDonald? Perhaps he had been watching us from across the loch, and had swam over to eat us. We stood thus some minutes, I all that time busy praying to Peter, Paul and my Guardian Angel, and a few others. Then at last the great lean dog just turned and slowly walked away amoung the rocks, Thank God I had ffriend. And thank God we had brought him & not the bich, for they say that a dog will protect his master against spirits, but that a bich will often side with them against him.

Still I left Donald sleeping. Our camp was in the safest place possible, at least, below the Winter's high water mark on the strand. I marked out a circle about us, and took ffriend in under my currach. I pray'd again, seven Our ffathers. I was hoping it was past mid night and ffriday behind us. ffriend was warm and calm. I think I fell asleep on the seventh Our ffather. But that was not the end of it! In my half sleep I coud still hear the lapping waves and I imagined I was hearing the Washing ffairy beating upon a rock the cloathes of children soon to die. And the sound of the burn close by was her sad song. My mind was still full of fairies!

At first light Donald woke me, and whiles we rowed down the loch I told him what I had seen. He said he was certain I had seen no gost dog but a wolf, and I believe now that he was right. The creature was too big for a dog. And I remember'd that the sheep had all scattered from the meadow – but it is well known that sheep take no heed of gosts. It had been a wolf, right enough, as my father described them. If so, no one from our Country has seen one since. If they are living yet, it must be in the high forests.

We came to land at our first chance, and put our currachs on our backs, & set out walking. I was not slow to be getting home, I can tell you. We were near to Swordland when I heard with joy the cock, the boy who blesses the morning. I knew no fairy nor any other being coud touch me now.

The sun was up as we climbed the path that drops over in to Brinacory, and we could hear the voices of the reapers allready at their work & their song in the Outfield, voices we knew. We skipt along to the tune of them. But I stopt short with my foot in the air when I caught sight of my mother standing in the door. I knew she would be boxing me about the ears, soon enough, in her joy at having me home. And so she did – nor did she leave Donald's neglected.

II

The White Island

It was that same year, two weeks after St Michael's day, that I went with Donald to live on the White Island. Let me tell you how it came about.

Mr James, the Irish priest, used to live there – he was the one who married my parents. He died when I was a year old, and after that the house there was rarely lived in. But every Summer Bishop James called the priests of the West to meet with him in it, & they used to come even from the far islands, unless some years the storms did not allow it. Lately he had been looking for a way to open a School somewhere in the Highlands, to train boys to be priests, because there was no such school in all of Scotland at that time, & he coud see that the White Island might be the very place for it. It was safe from enemies, for no Minister ever came into our Country, & he thoght that an island woud be a good place for a School – he used to say, 'That little strech of water will keep away the thistles & cares of the world'.

Well, that year he visited our Country again after Easter, & he broght three boys with him. He stay'd with them on the White Island untill the Summer, and that was how the School started. Then, when he himself had to leave to continue his own work,

he called in Mr George from the Low Countrey
to be the Master, & when he arrived he had three
more boys with him.

Donald was Brinacory's second son, & it had
been his mother's wish when she was alive that he
might become a priest. After she died his father had
kept her hope alive, for love of her. So when he
heard that the Seminary was started, allmost beside
his own door, he put the thoght to Donald that he
shoud make a try at it. He was just eleven at that
time, and his father knew that the other boys there
were older, so he asked my parents if they woud
be willing to let me go with him. He said that he
himself woud pay for my Schooling, & it woud be
schooling such as no boy unless a Gentleman's son
could ever think to get. He was remembering the
years when they had foster'd Donald. My parents
were willing, & I was for it allso, because it woud
keep me with my best friend & give me the chance
to learn how to read. As for Donald, he agreed to
go so long as he had me with him.

And that is how we found ourselves stepping into
the boat that Autumn morning. I was not quite
ten years old and I had never been so far down the
loch before, nor ever set eyes on the White Island.
There it lay before us, with a mistyness about its
shores, & to me it seem'd like a great water creature lurking there, lying low with only its back &
shoulders & its nose above the surface, as if it was
peering up the loch. I was wondering where we
coud land, and then we pulled round a low head-

land of rock & I saw a little sandy beach tucked away behind it, the beach that – they say – gives the island its name. It was a perfect, shelter'd place and (as I found out later) hardly ever the day when the wind got into it.

We stept out. Donald was gripping tightly to a blankett in which was tied whatever possessions we had broght with us. We looked about at our new home. Before us were two houses. The further one was small, & without a roof. The nearer one was bigger than my own house and byre together. It was built with alder & birch withies and sods, and it had a good row of stones along the bottom of the walls, built deeper on the side that faced the loch because the ground was low there. Near to them I saw where someone had made a start at building a wall of earth in the shape of a long square. I glanced back & saw that the man who had broght us over was allready half way hack to the land, & a sudden loneliness came on me. I took a breath & hurried to catch up with Donald. As we approached the house we coud hear voices coming from inside. Donald pulled open the door and we stood, unsure, on the threshold...,

... parvam, parvae, parvae, parva,
parvae, parvas, parvarum, parvis ...

There were six boys seated upon benches. I coud see the backs of their heads, and past them to a man standing before them. He glanced up, & then

continued marking time with a litle pointed wand.
Whether the boys heard us there I do not know,
but none turned, nor moved, nor ceased from his
chanting.

I looked about the room. To the left I cou'd see
an half dozen heather beds sett against the end wall,
& to the right a high fire place built with stones &
clay, with a wattle wall behind it that reached to
the roof. Beside it was a table with cups and dishes
on it. They looked unlike any dishes or cups that
I knew, for they were the first I had ever seen that
were not made of wood. But it was what was on
the wall at the Master's back that most caught my
eye. Our own house had a Cross upon the wall, of
course, made of rushes, like every other house in
our Country, before which we prayed every morning and night. But this was a Cross made of wood,
& carved with skill, with curls & scrolls on the
arms of it, & part of it was colored in gold so that
it shone in the light of the fir candles like a sunset.
And fixed upon it was the figure of Christ, white &
allmost naked, with marks of blood upon His head
& hands & feet, looking down at me with his head
on one side and eyes of sorrow & pain. I thoght it
the most wonderfull thing I had beheld in my life.
I coud not take my eyes off it. I do not know how
long I was standing there as if in a dream, but when
I came to myself again the boys were still at their
chanting –

> ... parva, parva, parva,
> parvorum, parvis, parvis.

Then the Master twiched his wand, as a signall for them to stop, & looked towards the door. At this every boy's head turned, and stared at Donald & myself where we stood in the doorway hesitating.

The Master smiled, and came forward & shook us by the hand gravely, as if we were men. Then he led us to the front & stood us there facing the boys, speaking to them and at the same time patting our shoulders, & anyone coud tell that he was talking about us. I heard the words 'Donald' and 'Ian', but these were the only ones that I recognised. Then he sett us on the second bench, & continued with the lesson.

I sat & looked about me, watching the scholars at their study. Sometimes the Master woud speak, and a boy woud stand & give an answer. Twice Donald whisper'd to me, but the second time the Master looked across at him, & we both sat up the straighter. I looked down at my brogs – they were the first pair I had ever had on my feet. My father had made them for me to go there in, and did I not feel the man in them? I watched the fir candles burning shorter, and the sky in the window turning towards dusk, & the figure on the cross growing darker. At last the Master spoke, and laid aside his book, and the boys all stood. The lesson was ended, and I had not understood a single word of it.

Now the boys set about preparing a meal, & each one seemed to know his task. As they busied themselves two of them spoke to us in our own language, & a third one smiled at us & said something in his language. Whenever the table was set ready we took our places beside it and stood waiting. All the while Donald & I were following whatever the others did. Now one boy said a Prayer, & at the end of it the rest all said 'Amen', & I said it just behind them – and this was the first word I had taken courage to utter since we left Glengarry's Morar. We sat down and began to eat, all save the Master; he stood & read to us from a book. No-one spoke thorow all the meal. Then he set aside the book and ate, whiles the rest of us sat silently untill he was finished. Then, at his nod, we rose from our seats, all as one, like birds rising from a tree.

The same two boys who had spoken to us before now told us to go with them. They had gather'd the dishes & cups, & we helped to carry them to the loch to wash. There was a flat rock placed by the water's edge for that purpose. The boys were asking us what were our families, and how old were we, and were we there to train for priests, or only to get schooling? The bigger of the two was Alan. He was sixteen, & allready taller than the Master. He was an Uist man, and his speech sounded strange to my ear. The other boy was Hugh. He too was a Clanranald, the brother of Morar, and he was a year younger than Alan.

'I have often looked across to your farm, for I was raised over in Mewboll', he said, 'not like this man who has journeyed to us from afar out of the

'Western Sea!'

I liked them both, but I liked Hugh especially – allready I was hoping that he woud become my friend.

The Master's name was Mr George, they told us.

'George the First & Last we call him', said Hugh. 'He does not have our language; nor have the three boys who come from the East. That is why all the lessons are done in English. But you will pick it up quickly enough'.

'I guessed that was what you were all speaking before', said Donald.

'Oh no', said Alan, 'that was Latin. But you will learn that soon enough allso!'

'Do not be worrying!' said Hugh to me with a laugh, for I believe he could see in my face that I was feeling about as uncertain & out of my world as if I had fallen asleep & found myself in the company of the ffairies.

We picked up the cups & dishes, and it was then that I learned that a dish made of baked clay breaks if you drop it. I thoght of the Master, & I believe if I had had a boat I woud have row'd home there & then.

Now all the boys had their tasks finished and were coming out for Recreation. They gather'd round us, whiles Hugh & Alan were telling them about us in English, Then they shew'd us the earth wall that they were making to enclose a garden. They took us to the small house, which was to be the Chapell whenever the Master woud get a roof tree & roof beams to finish it. They shew'd us the best fishing place, over the rocks facing Glengarry's Countrey, and it was there as we looked over the loch that a bell suddenly sounded out at our backs, so that Donald & I allmost leapt into the water, but the boys said that this was just the signall that Recreation was ended.

We returned to the house then, & broght the benches over against the fire, for it was the time for reading from the Lives of the Saints. Hugh whisper'd that the book was the Life of Francis Xavier. Mr George began to read. Twice he stopt and called one of the older boys forward to take a turn, which they did but haltingly, & then he woud continue himself. At last he laid it aside, & every one gathered round the Crucifix for Night Prayers. Each gave a quick nod of his head towards it, & then knelt down and closed his eyes to begin. I knelt down beside them, dropping down on my right knee, with my arms resting across the left one, the way I was broght up to. But when I opened one eye in the midst of the Prayers I saw that the rest were kneeling with their two knees upon the floor, & I quickly changed to that way whiles all their eyes were still shut. And that is how I have done it ever since − I think I am about the only man in Glengarry's Morar who kneels that way.

After prayers each boy went his own way. One lay upon his bed. A couple of others sat beside the fire, and Hugh and Alan went outside to walk. I follow'd at their heels, and I started to ask Hugh if

I might walk with them, but he put his finger to his lipps & shook his head at me. I coud not guess what he intended, nor woud he in any wise tell me, and I returned to the house wondering how I had offended him and if he woud ever be my friend again.

It was dark when we went to our rest. They had broght in more heathers for Donald & me, and I was given a place with him on one side of me, & Hugh on the other. There were large stones set upon the heathers, close to our heads, to mark our spaces. I lay down. The fire was smother'd; the fir candles were put out. Soon I coud hear the breathing of the boys as one by one they fell asleep. I knew Donald was not sleeping by the way he turned now & then, & once he reached across and touched my shoulder. I guessed that his mind was full of thoghts, like my own. It was only the second night of my life that I had slept out of my own house. I lay in the blackness, & I began to think of that other night. But at once I said to myself, 'You are quite safe here. Mr George is close by, in the small room behind the wattle fence. There have allways been priests here in this house. The whole island is a place of prayer & holinesss. No evil thing would dare to set foot upon its shore, nor fly above it'. And so I fell asleep.

But my sleep was full of dreams. I dreamt that I was sitting with Donald in the front of a boat, looking back to the shore as it slipt away, and we further & further from our homes. Before our eyes were the backs of the heads of six boys, as they sat on the cross benches and row'd to the rhithm of the chanting of Latin, & the Master in the stern standing facing them with his wand. And then terror began to come upon me to see the shore so far away & allmost disappearing from sight, and I tried to whisper my fear to Donald, but the Master looked up sternly at me. I tried to whisper to Hugh on the bench in front of me, but he turned with his finger upon his lips & shook his head. At last I tried to stop them rowing away in the only manner that I coud think of – I dropt a dish upon a rock as we past by it, & made it smash. But still the Master paid no heed. So I dropt an other, then a third, & a fourth. He looked up fearcely, but I was ready to drop every dish, & every cup, now – and there must have been twenty of them. I dash'd them down one by one, untill as I was dropping the last one the Master began to ring his bell, and he order'd Hugh to seize & shake me, and with the ringing & the shaking I awoke.

I looked about me. There was hardly a glint of light in the window. The fir candles were out, all but one. The smother'd fire had been uncovered and was just beginning to catch, with a ring of white ash around it. I coud see the dark shapes of boys pulling on their brogs and moving here & there, their shadows creeping along the walls. But if they were moving, there were none of them speaking, and I had sense enough to keep silent myself.

Hugh beckoned me to follow him. We went to the loch, I feeling the way with my feet upon the path at his back. The rest of the boys were there already. The moon was hid, but I cou'd hear them splashing, & just make out their crouching forms as they took their morning wash.

We got back to the house and knelt before the Crucifix, & when at last we rose my knees were well ready for rising. No sooner were we on our feet than Hugh & Alan began to tell us that this was their day to prepare the Breakfast, & that Donald & I might help them if we liked. At first I was not certain if it was permitted for me to speak in reply, but it was then that Hugh told us about the Great Silence.

'It begins as soon as Night Prayers are over', he said. 'From that moment no-one may speak a word, not even Mr George, unless it is absolutely needfull, untill after Prayers upon the morrow. That was why I coud not explain it to you last night. But it is over now, and we may talk as much as we like untill Lesson time'.

After Breakfast we had our morning Recreation, or 'Freedom' as the boys called it. And then the bell sounded for lessons. The Master had appointed Hugh to be the Monitor for Donald & myself, to explain the lessons to us untill we had enough English to understand them for ourselves. Hugh told us that we woud be learning Arithmetick, History and Rhetorick that morning, & in the afternoon Scripture, Doctrine and Latin, and that this was the same every day, unless sometimes we woud learn Geography in stead of History. He tried to

explain what these names meant, & he told us allso
that there were no lessons after noon on Wednes-
days, but Long Recreation in stead, & none at all
on Sundays.

Well, the lessons lasted all morning, with barely
a word spoken, unless it was Mr George asking a
question, or a boy reciting, or all of them together
chanting the tables of Arithmetick. Then we took
our noon meal, and after it another spell of Freedom. And then the bell called us back for Manual
Labour. This was the time when we had to build
the garden wall. Hugh said that they had been at
it since the Summer, every dry day, but it was not
even half done. We worked with spades & basketts
without rest untill the bell rang out again, but when
I threw aside my spade & looked at the little patch
of fresh dug earth it seemed that we had added allmost nothing to what was done before. I wonder'd
would it ever be finished, as we washed in the loch
& went indoors for lessons.

The first one was Scripture, then Doctrine. But
before we began the Latin the Master lit fir candles
round the walls, as the sun went down and shadows began to fill the corners of the room. And so
at last we came to Supper, and I for my part woud
happily have eaten the White Horse of the Loch.

So now I have described to you one whole day
& night round in my new life. And that was the
way it was, each day pretty well the same, as the
Autumn went out and the Winter came in.

That Winter was long and lonely for me, and many

the day at Freedom time I woud wander to the highest place on the island & gaze into the East towards my home. The other islands hid it from my view. But I woud run my eye along the hills of Glengarry's Morar, and just before they disappear'd behind the edge of Middle Island I could see the clifts that stand high above our farm, & make out the gully where the stream begins that divides East & West Brinacory. And I woud follow it down in my imagination. And where it tumbles down below our shielding, close by where the Priest's Burn joins it, I woud see in my mind's eye my brothers & sister playing there; and then where it runs slower betwixt the corn fields I woud picture my mother taking water from it; and where it meets the loch beside the Bay of Drowning I woud imagine my father in his currach fishing.

Often those days were hatefull to me, when I could hardly understand a thing about me. But after the New Year, as the evenings grew longer & my English better, I began to look forward to the lessons, unless maybe Arithmetick. It was History and Geography I waited for the most, for the books we read & the stories that the Master told to us carried me away to antient ages and far distant places of the world. Every day I discover'd new things & new thoghts, and for me the days began to fly by, and hardly ever did the home sickness settle on me now.

But I knew that it was not so for Donald. He was always restless during the lessons, & he only

1715

seemed to come awake at Recreation. He loved to sport, and to break the Rules, and soon he got the name of 'Donald of the Tricks'. He was for ever being scolded by the Master, who was not a great one for jokes. The two of them were like fish oil & water when they were in each other's company.

In the sunny days of Spring we found a hundred things to do to fill our times of Freedom. Some days we ran races right round the Island. Some days we would be pitching the Stone of Strength, or playing Monster Catch the Slowest One. If there was heat in the sun we woud bathe – three of us had the art of swimming, and we woud swim across to Little Island & the rest woud follow, one rowing the currach & the others hanging on to it. If the sky was grey we might fish, & hope to catch enough for Friday's supper. And when the wind blew strong with rain in it we wou'd sit on our heels in the lea of the house, & maybe just throw dice there. I recall many a time we woud be at play and the Master going about his work, and I wou'd see him stop & stand watching us, with a smile of approval, his hands upon his hips and his black cassock flapping at his anckles. He used to say that Recreation was just as important for us as our Lessons or Manual Labour, and allmost as important as our Prayers. He said that we woud need strength of body, as well as strength of mind & soul, to face the life that lay ahead of us.

'Living here among friends', he told us once, 'you cannot have any imagination of the trialls you will

endure when you are sent onto the Mission, You
will be giving up everything you might have hoped
for as the sons of Gentlemen. You will have no
home, but will live from day to day in the homes of
others. Your labours will never cease, night or day,
& every day of your lives you will wake to the fear
of arrest. For there will be neighbors beside you
who will think it a good deed to deliver you into
the hands of our Enemies, & to take the reward for
doing so. Even our own people may be tempted
to betray you – 500 Merks is a great temptation.
And some are sure to abjure their ffaith, in spite
of all your work and prayers. For the Law is that
any man who professes the Catholick religion must
lose all that he owns, and there are some gentlemen – more to be pitied than condemn'd – who do
not have it in them to make that sacrifice, & woud
sooner embrace Heresie than give up their possessions. Most, thank God, remain true, & will readily
take you into their homes. But if so, never leave
your Vestments or any other thing there. Carry
them away with you allways. This very year men
have been drag'd to prison when something left by
the priest was found in their house. You yourselves
will learn to be men of many parts & many arts,
many travells & many temptations. But remember
& carry with you daily the words of holy Scripture
– "Fear not, I go before you allways" – and great
will be your joy, in this life & the next.'

These were amazing words to me, who had never
in my life met anyone who was not of our ffaith,

nor knew of the existence of any enemy, nor ever imagined that there was any other way of living than the way we lived.

At the end of the Summer the two oldest boys, Alan & John, left us. They were sent over the sea to Rome and we never saw them on the Island after that. Then Donald went home to help get the harvest in, and once he was away Hugh was the only one left to whom I coud speak in our language. We were waiting for Donald to return, but Michaelmass went by without him. And then word came that he was not for coming back, and I knew then that I allso woud have to leave. It was exactly a year I had been there. I believe my going was a disappointment to Mr George, for he had held high hopes of me because I was an apt pupil. For myself, I was glad & sad at once to be leaving. I went home to my family, and to ffriend, but for many a day after I woud still wake before the sparrow, and sit bolt upright in my bed listening for the ringing of the bell.

It was just at this time that the Highlandmen had risen to fight against the English King & bring back our own King James. I well recall my mother's brother James, and my father's brother Malcolm each taking his sword and targe down off the wall, & joining the rest on the road to Sherriff Muir, with Brinacory leading them. I recall allso how after the battle there our enemies were hunting down the priests, just as Mr George had fore-

told. Old Bishop Thomas was captured & thrown
into prison, & Bishop James & most of the priests
were in hiding. My father said it was certain that
the Seminary woud be closed allso, but Mr George
stay'd there with the boys all thorow the Winter
and into the next year. He judged that they were   1716
in the safest place, sett betwixt the snow amoung
the mountains to the East & the storms upon the
sea in the West. But as soon as the snow melted &
the Spring storms were past he knew it was too
dangerous to stay. And so, as soon as they had celebrated the ffeast of Easter he closed the school &
sent the boys home. I believe Hugh and a couple of
the others went back to live at Mewboll farm, and
Mr George kept in touch with them & with the
rest, in the hope that they might yet start again.

Well, a full year went by, untill he returned. And   1717
then it was not to bring them back to the White
Island − he said that the place was too dangerous
now, being so close to the sea. But there was a
house, called Scalan, far away in the East beyond
our mountains, in a valley high amoung hills in the
Country of the Gordons, where they woud be pro-
tected from enemies, and it was there that he meant
to start the School again. He said that the rest of
the boys were allready there, all but Hugh and the
two who were at Mewboll with him, and he had
come to bring them there allso, along with some
things from the house, if their families were willing. He planned to make two journeys, because of
all that had to be carried, and to take one boy on

the first journey and the other two on the second. He asked my father if I might go with them on the first journey, in order to help them lead the horses, & to be a companion for himself on the road back. I pled with my father to let me go, for I thoght it my chance to set eyes on some of those far places in the world that our books had told us of, & when he saw the shining in my eyes he agreed.

Two horses we had, each with two baskets. Into these we were to pack the cups, dishes & knives, some plaids and blanketts, the vestments & vessels, the Crucifix, and a few cloathes & other things. The books we left for the second journey.

It was the day after May day when we sett out, heading first for my own farm. My family were waiting at the door, & they knelt for the Blessing. My mother had butter fresh made for our journey, wrap'd in a cloth, & she gave it into the hands of Mr George.

'We did not look for it', said he as he thanked her.

'It will have the more luck in it for that', she answer'd.

I saw with pride how handsome she was, standing near as tall as my father, in the striped Arasaid that all the women of our farm still wore in those days.

'May the fair Mary keep you & guide you your whole road!' were her parting words.

We made our way towards the head of the loch, & it was soon clear to me that we wou'd be in need of all the guidance that Mary coud spare us. Mr George was a learned man, right enough, but he had learned nothing of mountains. A girl woud have been more use than he at leading a horse, or sleeping on the hill. I coud tell that he was frightened of every clift we came to, and so coud the horses – they were not at their ease with him at all. And Duncan, the other boy with us, was not a great deal better. It was as well they had me with them.

We were ten days journeying, upon hill sides, thorow glens, & beside lochs great & small, untill we came into a long, wide Vallie that ran North. I saw that the houses there were not thatched in the manner that ours are, but with hay; and the horses were not bearing their loads on their backs, but drawing them along the ground in baskets tied upon poles. The cattle were sickly to the eye, and the men there were allready talking of the Plague.

Then we left that country and climbed again, and journey'd two days more along high glens amoung smooth, dark hills. At last we enter'd a wide, flat countrey, with great walls of heathery hills to the East & South, and came to a halt at the house of Scalan farm. It was made out of turves, & stood upon a narrow shelf of ground. Behind it was a litle river flowing North, not like the mountain streams I knew for it seemed to run along the top of the flat meadow like a silver ribbon laid there. Before the house was a low, round hill, with clumps of Junipers on it, and a long, straight field running up it allmost to the top. Further down the glen were the corn fields of other farms, but they were not yet grown so tall as the fields of my home.

We stayed three days there, and in all that time I never saw the tops of the hills, nor the sun. The glen seemed to me like a place enclosed & hidden, from which the outside world & all its enemies were shut out. It was a cold & gray place, & far from the sea. I listen'd for the voice of the thrush, or the song of the gull, but I heard only the black-cock, & the curlew's lonely cry. I could not wait to be away. On the fourth day Mr George & I sett out again, leading our horses back the long way we had come. But now all the countries we entered were full of the cattle plague, and hardly a farm we came to but we saw beasts lying dead beside the road.

As we came near to our own Country we were looking out for the red sodgers who had been encamped there all that Summer, searching for any one who had fought for James. But they were gone. They had carried away one or two swords when they left, but all the good bright ones had been kept hid under the thatch.

Now again we were left in peace, and for a few years our lives were without incident, so I will pass quickly over that time, when I was growing to manhood.

1720 But one thing I must tell you about, that happened just after I reached sixteen. It was two or three days before Christmas Eve, on a fine, cold evening, with a white frost on its way & the sky full of stars. I had wearied of the talk & the songs in the house, and was strolling on the path with Donald & his sister Mary, and my old dog ffriend. I think I had an eye for Mary at the time. And of a sudden, whiles we were talking there, a shooting star flew out from behind the hill above us and rushed across the sky into the South. It was bigger and brighter by far than any I ever saw, and it stayed in our sight longer than shooting stars do, & I give you my word I coud hear the Swish of it. We all of us duck'd our heads, even ffriend! Mary said it must have been a special Christmas star sent to remind us of the birth of Jesus. But a couple of mounths later word came that a son had been born to our rightfull King James in his exile, so that he had an heir at last. And it turned out that the birth was on the very same day that we had seen the star. A good few others had seen it allso, on both sides of the loch, and we all took it for a sign that this Prince was given to us by God, & woud one day be our King.

The Winter when I reached nineteen was the worst 1723
for frost & snow that I ever remember. It was the death of several in our Country, and my own father was one of them. He took a rheum in the chest after getting the milch cow in off the hill on New Year's night, and he never recover'd from it. In the 1724
last week of his life you could hear the water in his body as he breathed, and I mind the litle children of our neighbors standing in our door listening, fascinated by the sound. He died on the first day of

Lent, may God be mercifull to him.

1725   In the Autumn of the next year my friend Hugh return'd into the West, with a white collar at his neck. He had been living at Scalan all the time since I saw him last, & he had finished his schooling there, and had just that Summer been made a priest. He was the first man to be ordained in his own land, without going to the Colleges over sea. And now Bishop James had sent him straight back to be amoung his own people. For a year he

1726   stayed down in Moydart, and learned the work of a priest there, and when he was judged ready he came over to our countrey. He took the house on the White Island to be his home, with a boat of his own pulled up on the beach there, so that he could easily get over to all the farms of Glengarry's and Morar's Morar.

III

Miner and drover

When I was aged three and twenty, word came 1728 to our country from a trading vessell that an ore called Lead had been found in the hills of Sunnart, and that those who owned the mines were seeking men to labour there. I made up my mind to try for it.

I went for absolution to Mr Peter who was staying in those days in Morar, tho' he was not our own priest. It was said that he had been a sodger and a school master in the East, and was once a Protestant. I believe that the homesickness was on him in our country, as well as the lonelyness of his priest's life. Many the time we saw him with drink taken, and he near died once in a ditch returning from a wedding.

Having no other to go with me I set out alone one dry day of Autumn. I had with me my parents' blessing, and food enough for a week, and a leathern scabard with a knife and fork inside it from Donald, Brinacory's son. Calum row'd with me over to Mewboll and there I headed South into the hills. I knew that my journey woud take me thorow Clanranald's country by muir, bill and coast to the river of Shiel, and from there to Sunnart Loch near to whose head were the mines of Strontian. Of the distance I had no knowledge − for all I knew it might be fifty miles, or three times fifty.

I met with little wind or rain upon the road, and cross'd every river without danger, and came to the end of the land at a stroll on the evening of the second day. And there at the loch side I slept. All that was to do now was to make my way towards the head of it; but I coud not believe how long were those last miles. After every hill I climbed, an other hill rose up before me. The day was past noon, and still no sign of the place I sought. I follow'd a stream up in to a muir that rose to a summit, and at the top I look'd over − below lay a broad glen. I descended above the shieldings and the fields, untill I reached a tumbling burn. I was still half way up on the hill, and far away below on my right hand the Loch sparkled in the sun. Now I struck a path leading further up the hill, which show'd every sign of much use. It was like no path I had experienced in my life time, for instead of being rutted in the centre it was ridged in the centre and rutted at either side − I could make no guess at the reason or the use of it. I follow'd it in to a wood, near creeping with wearyness, and there I met a boy & asked him was I any way near to the Country where I might find the lead mine of Strontian.

'You are not a hundred steps from it', said he, and as I broke out of the wood and ascended to a ridge of rock, there it lay before me.

I cou'd not describe it to you. Never had I seen such a gathering of men, and hutts, & beasts. It was as I imagined a great city might be, or the camp of an army. I stood still on the edge of it for long enough in wonder. But then recalling my purpose I ask'd to see the one who own'd the place.

'You will hardly do that', said a man to me, 'you must speak to the man in the Office', and he pointed me the way. There I was told that they would give me work, and that I shoud begin my tasks on the morrow. Then I was sent to a much larger house, made all of timber logs. Inside were frames sett against the walls, with spaces for men to sleep in, one beside the next, with others above and above again, so that at night they look'd like a honey comb with grubs in it. To each man was alotted a hole, and I was given mine.

There were five houses the same as this one, set in a row. Standing apart from them higher upon the hill was the house of the Manager, built of stone with a roof of black slates, the first I ever saw. Across an open space stood a high, square bigging of stone which they called the Miln. The door of it was open & I stept inside: there were four hearths in it, for the smelting of ore. Beside it were three peat stacks, each worth six of any stack at home. There were other biggings here and there – stables, stores for creels and barrels, a hut where a woman sold meat & bread & whiskey & ale, and an other where were kept the pick axes & ropes. I coud not count the number of men who were there, and like bees each man seem'd to know his task. At a place in the edge of the hill great Ditches had been dug on a down wards slope, so that if you walked into one you stood below the level of the land to the depth of three men. Here a score of men were digging in to the earth – they were wearing trews like Gentlemen, but with naked backs. As each man dug a second lifted the ore upon his spade & threw it in to a waggon by his side. There were three waggons, and it was them above all else that caught my attention. They had woven baskets like the ones I had seen on the road to Scalan, but these were not drawn on poles but upon wheels. If I tell you that never in my life before had I cast eyes upon a wheel, nor heard the name of one, you will understand my wonder. What I saw now were four round cut timbers, one at each corner, set upon axle trees so that they might revolve, and as they revolved they woud roll across the earth, so that a man or a horse might draw the waggon with ease over plain ground, even tho' it was laden. So I worked it out. And now I understood the path with the two rutts, and I noticed that there were a number in the camp, along which the wheel'd carts coud be drawn. One led to the river, and there instead of a ford it cross'd high above it on timbers built level on piles of hewn oak. I was not for asking questions and shewing my innocence, but for listening & learning. And this too was some thing new, for the only bridge I ever saw till then was a tree laid across a burn. Altogether I learned a few new names and saw a few new sights that day, I can tell you. I stood with my eyes fixt upon the bridge & the basckets with wheels untill the sun went down.

This was my life for six mounths, high on the hill among the clouds and snow and the darkness of Winter. My task was shovelling, and some times digging. I was put in a team with a man from Mull, Colin McQuarry was his name, a short, strong fair haired man. He was a Protestant, as he told me all Mull men are. We grew to be close friends. I never met a more honest or clean speaking man. It was easy to tell that he missed his wife and children.

Upon occasion we saw the managers, looking over the work in one part or an other, and once I past two who were said to be the owners of the Company. They were speaking in the English toungue, of the great costs and the little results, and the difficulty of comptrolling so great a gathering of men, and for sure they thoght no one standing by understood their conversation. One of them was a tall, lean Irishman, Wade was his name; I heard later that he was Chief of the red coated army of all Scotland.

I was thoght well of, any way, and when I left 1729 in the Spring with money enough in my purse I was told I woud be welcomed back. And that was my full intention. I came home to our farm the worldly wise one, full of my knowledge of wonders and of mankind. I told our neighbours that I was for returning to the mining after the harvest. But it was two years before I went again, & there was a reason or two for this. And one of the reasons was Peggy.

I was on the road to Tarbert on a clear, frosty morning of Autumn. As I walk'd thorow the farm of Swordland I heard a woman singing at the milking, and I determined without hesitation to find out who it was. And when approching I caught sight of her, her sleeves above the elbow as I remember clearly and her bare feet tuck'd in, lovely brown haired, not seeing me, I vow'd at once that I would win her at all costs. I was allready imagining in that moment that she woud be my wife! Still she did not see me, and then when she began to sing the verse 'Bring back the cattle Donald & you will get a loving wife', I woud not have hesitated there & then to change my name to Donald!

She told me she had come there from Knoidart. We were not closely related. She shew'd me one of her cows that had a sore on the udder & would not give milk. I knew a remedy for it, which I told her, to hold a lighted peat close to the teat and so to soften it. She thanked me, & if she spoke little I thoght her eyes told a tale that I might take courage from.

1730   After that it was surprising how often I had cause to pass thorow Swordland, and how often we came across each other there. Any way, by that Summer we were courting. Often we woud sit above Srone Gower looking across to moon lit Mewboll and Clanranald's country. It was a bonny place but a dangerous one in the darkness. She used to sing to me her own songs, and with a smile one that I asked her to sing –

My darling brown girl of the cattle . . .
My darling brown girl of the smiling eye,
I am not bent upon deceiving you.

She sang it often that Summer. But of all her songs the one that was my favorite thorow all our years together was the song she first sang under the cow.

We would part by the rock at the boundary of her fields, and then I had the journey home. At one place, whensoever the water of the loch was high, I must climb round the cliff where heather ropes were fix'd for this purpose. Then I must cross the burn that is haunted. Only Peggy cou'd have drawn me to do these things in the night. She used to stand to watch me out of sight – they say it is bad luck to look back, but I allways did, & my life with Peggy was all good fortune.

So it was the second Spring ere I return'd to Stron- 1731
tian. I was eager for the old familiar sights and sounds, and some were there still all right. But so much I found changed. The place was bigger even than before, and new men own'd it – the York Building Company they were called. They had found a fresh seam of good ore, wider than the first & a full two miles long, greater than any other known in the world. But it lay deep in the earth & hard to reach, so that shafts had been dug down, with ladders, and the men must now do their digging in tunnells under the ground. The old Grooves

where we used to dig were neglected, & up beside them were wooden Barracks for the new men, for as many as three thousand now labor'd there. The Barracks they called 'New York', and there I slept and ate. My task was to build roads of stone for the new furnaces, and it was here that I met up again with Colin. He had been at the mines on & off ever since we had last labor'd together. The greater furnace could swallow as many creels of ore as a man coud unload in half a day, and it roar'd on the dark nights. It was fired with logs and coals broght in from the sea to timber keys that had been new built on the loch side. Three men had been drown'd in the building of them. But it was a week's work for a whole gang of men to draw them up onto the hill, so that the fire-men preferred, if they could get away with it, to use logs cut from the wood close by.

And that was where the trouble was for me. Hatred had grown for the miners amongst the tenants of the farms, because they had been destroying the woods, not to speak of killing beasts and trampling corn down in the vallie, taking the fish from off their very hooks, & even it was said one had outraged a woman of that place. I knew the talk in the barracks at nights, and I could well believe that some of the men were apt for such crimes.

But of these things I thoght nothing as I stroll'd abroad one warm Spring evening with a purse full of the money of a week's labor. I was amongst woods & passing beneath a crag when, of a sudden, five men stood in my road. My back was against the rock, they with a dirk each and I with no time nor space to draw my own. It was 'All the dogs down upon the strange dog', & I was like to lose my money if not my life itself. Then, from where I do not know, Colin was at my side, and an other man with him, both armed. This second man they seem'd to know, & have a fear for. They hesitated, which gave me allso the chance to arm myself. They back'd away, with eyes on my new ally betwixt threat and retreat, one muttering some thing about 'the pup of a Uist dog and a Morvern bitch'. And then they were gone.

This man was Alexander and his home was near to ffinnan's Island. He was the master of the Protestant school down there, and a tester of their Catechism thorow the countries of Sunnart and Ardnamurchan.

It was his work to teach & test the miners as well as the tenants of the land, & so it was that he was known to many. His father had been known & fear'd before him.

After this Colin and I both decided to finish with the mining. He got home on a coal vessell and I never saw him again. Likely he is dead long since – may God be mercifull to him if so. For my part, I believed that those who had near kill'd me once might try again. So when Alexander said that he would go with me by an other road, over by the hill of Drum Glass & down to his own home by ffinnan's Island, I was not for preventing him. And so we set out North together. I came to know him well upon the journey; we were suited to each other's company. He spoke to me of his beliefs, and asked me about mine; these things seem'd a matter of great interest to him.

I staid two days & nights with himself and his wife. A tidy house she kept, with a fresh hew'n stone dike round it. They had two children at that time, both dark like himself; I mind their names yet – Ronald was aged to walk, & Jeanie was still at the breast. It was the kind of home I hoped to set up soon myself. And that increased my haste to be away; I was impatient to be back with Peggy. I had a new song for her that I learn'd from Alexander – he was a bard of fame even then and they were his own verses –

> *Tho' melodious the fiddle*
> *With its strings tightly stretch'd*
> *'Tis the lass of the shielding*
> *Sets the dance in my heart ...*
> *It woud dazle your eye*
> *On the dewy May morn,*
> *The threads of her ringlets*
> *In the rays of the sun.*

When I got home I told her that I had composed them my self, and she thoght I was the great poet! As to Alexander, it was my hope that we woud meet again. I was in his debt, and I was minded to repay him some day.

That Spring I asked Peggy wou'd we be married, & she consented, if she wou'd gain permission. So I made arrangement to visit her home with Donald, Brinacory's son, to discuss the matter with her father. When we arrived and went inside Peggy was seated back by the wall, & her father Michael out at the fire. He was a tall & flourishing man even then, with cheeks as red as the foxglove, as the saying is. Donald did the talking, as was custom. I sat on the long bench with my hands on my lapp. They talked long enough, for sure, and the sun passed beyond the window, but when Michael at last broght out the whiskey in the ram's horn Peggy came out of the shaddows and sat beside me smiling.

Now we had the work of preparing for a marriage and a home. I had money from the mining, and there would be more soon from the selling of our cattle, for every year after May day a dealer from the Low Country used to arrive at our farms to buy. John Grant was his name. He had an agreement with Glengarry that we woud sell onely to him, and he paid fair prices. He had our language for he was born in the mountains. He was known and trusted – he had been coming to our country for near twenty years, and he allways broght us news from the outside world. He did his own droving, paying a couple of men & may be a boy from one of the farms to go with him. Well, this year, as we drank together after the selling, he told me of the drove, and the great trist at the town of Crief, and of the money and the adventure in it, and he ask'd me would I go? The money I needed, and as the drink went down and did its work the adventure beckon'd too.

So it was that we teamed together, with a third man named Michael from one of the farms of Stouil. We had fifty beasts to drive, every one a four year old in good condition – & three of the best of them were from our own farm. I got new brogs for the journey and cut holes in them, which I was glad of when we got amongst the muirs. I was to take otter skins that Calum had trap'd, for John said they fetched a good price in the town of Crief. My mother wanted one or two things for the house. She had set her heart upon a crusy lamp, for she had seen one at Brinacory's house. And I had it in mind to get a thing or two for my own new home also.

Before I would make such a journey I went down to the White Island for absolution. There was a new priest staying there, whom I had not met before. My friend Hugh had been living there six years, since being ordain'd priest. But last year he had left us and journey'd to France, the reason we did not yet know, and this new man had been broght to our Continent from the island of Uist to take his place. He had arrived in the Summer, & it was from him I got absolution. He allso gave to me a letter for the Bishop in Edinburgh, which I was to hand on privately to a man in Crief, and he told me exactly where this man might be found, and that the letter must not fall in to any other man's hands.

And so we set out on the week before Michaelmass. Peggy had given me her father's whiskey horn. My mother embraced me with bright eyes.

'Remember the people you come from', she said, 'and wheresoever you go on the road bring no bad word of yourself home.'

We gather'd the beasts at Tarbert, and there we join'd with men driving a herd of thirty from Sleat and others with near the same number from Eig. Together we faced East for Ardnamurach and the head of Loch Nevish, and then up and up amongst the rocks and clifts. John led the first ten ahead, and kept at their back to stop them turning. He trusted to let them find the safe way themselves, and all the other hundred follow'd the road these ones chose. So like a snake we made our winding way over and down in to Glen Dessary, and there where the road was wider the beasts spred out. John took the dry roads where he could, and staid clear of the farms. He never joumey'd after the sun set, and allways an hour before that he went ahead to arrange our station for the night. He knew well the Gentlemen of every glen, so that each night we slept without payment or black meall or fear of attack.

We journey'd the length of Loch Arcaig and cross'd the river close by the house of Lochiel. Thence we moved South wards untill we reached a wider river than any we had met so far. Here we waited, for a great herd was at the shore ahead of us. Cattle from Island Sky they were, and others that had come over into Sky from Uist. They had all swum the Kyles to Bernera, roped jaw to tail an half dozen together at a time. Four hundred had come over on the up tide in one day, their drovers told us, and not one lost.

We crossed the river behind them. It was running fast, & the bed of it was broken up by all their trampling. We had to take our beasts across a few at a time. We made ten journeys alltogether, using our sticks to keep our feet and each man gripping the next with his free arm. 'The Clans of the Gael shoulder to shoulder!' as John said.

For a day we follow'd the heels of the Sky men thorow fertile lands, with great snowy mountains on our right side, and then we turned up a glen and in to those mountains. For five days then we saw scarce a tree, leaning in to the wind and the Autumn snow, with allways the huge black herd an hour's journey ahead of us. John slow'd our pace. If we sweated the beasts or damaged them now we woud lose them or get no price for them. When at last we came down from the muir of Rannoch and in to a broad glen we rested them. And many of them we shoe'd. We had the shoes and nails with us with this in mind, and it was a full day's work. On most we put four shoes, but on some whose condition was worse we put eight. Three of them we were obliged to slaughter.

We journey'd now thorow glens, untill on the evening of the fifteenth day John told us that on the morrow we woud reach the town of Crief. We made our station upon a sloping meadow with a stream beside it. To our left and before us were low wooded hills, and upon our right hand a wide & level glen with a low ridge beyond. Behind us were the last of the bare, heathery mountains. We had come into the Low Country! And I was about to make my bed in it!

In the morning I awoke before the others, and I took a stroll. I leap'd over the stream. All was still & empty. I met a girl in the field & asked her the miles to the town of Crief, but she answer'd in words I could not catch and ran from me. I learn'd after from John that the small stream that I had leap'd across divided the country of Erse from that of English, and that day as we journey'd forwards children were calling after us allways in the English toungue.

It was a day for our wands, for now the road was fill'd with herds, mingling and making for the town, At noon we cross'd the slow, wide river, close to where an other river joins it as it turns South wards in a great bend. Within that bend is a meadow land, and this was the place of the trist.

Well, we knew it before we saw it – at two miles distance we coud hear it, and as we came over the last hill the whole land lay black before us, with a fog of steam above it. John said he believed that as many as twenty thousand cattle might be sold, and surely most of them were gather'd there that day. On the meadow there were dikes so that herds coud be kept together, but many a stray wander'd here and there. On the river side not a blade of grass was to be seen. Where the land rose at the far edge of the meadow there were set huts of woven willow branches, and here men were selling – one bread, an other meat and broth, and an other ale. Here allso tinkers were selling the spoons and broches and needles they make from silver, horn or bone. In other hutts sat men who exchanged money and bills of promise. In others were men willing to buy as well as sell and it was here I sold my skins.

We watched as John went about the selling of the beasts. He seem'd acquainted with every Low Country dealer, and many a Highland man too. He listen'd to each man's offer. He went from one to an other. He began to make up his mind. And even then he waited, as a man does who has a fish at the hook. If you haul him in too soon (he said) you get a low price. But if you leave him too long you may lose him. And if you lose too many, & find your self with the beasts still on your hands & the fair packing up, you may in the end have to sell for next to nothing. John was getting offers of two hundred Shillings, but near the end of the day, with drink to argue for him, he got a man to agree to two hundred & thirty. They touch'd thumbs to seal it.

I was glad that he had struck so good a price. I had form'd no liking for the Low Country men, from what I saw of them. They were dull of heart & greedy and it was easy to see that they held the Highland men in scorn. I was glad he bested them.

It was late when we went to our rest, and the night still as full of noise as if it was day. Great fires had been lighted here and there, and the faces of men & cattle could be seen amoung the shadows. As I lay on the earth I caught now the smell of wood smoke, and now of tobbacco or ale or broth, and allways and above every other the smell of the cattle. My friends had drink taken, but not I, since I was holding the money. I lay long awake as at last the camp grew quiet, with now and then the lowing of a beast or the voices of drunk men picking their way amongst the sleepers.

In the dead of the night I awoke & stood up and look'd about me. The fires were near spent. There was one dim light in the town over the river. Far to the North I coud see the nearest hills of the Highlands. I thought of Peggy, and my kin, sleeping beyond & beyond those great muirs. I felt more lonely than I could have felt if I had been in the New World beyond the ocean. I thoght with dread of dying & being buried in this place.

On the morrow John paid us our wages and we parted, he heading home to the town of ffalkirk. I deliver'd my letter, and got my mother her lamp, and some fine horn spoons and wooden cups for Peggy, four of each. With money in my purse I was not for journeying alone, nor for crossing the muir of Rannoch, so Michael and I join'd up with the Sky men and took a different road.

Now this was a road such as you never saw in your life. From the very town of Crief it ran, allmost to the edge of Glengarry's country. It was as wide as a house, made plain with stones and gravel all the way. It had a bank & a ditch on either side, and it ran straight, wheresoever. The red coated sodgers had built it the Summer before for moving their army against the men of the Highlands.

We made great speed upon it, any way. Often it follow'd close by the course of rivers, but on the fourth day it rose up & took us on to a great hill that stood before us. The place they call Corry Arack, and it was wonderfull how the road was builded upon this hill. It turned to and fro in zig zag for the steepness. Upon the one side it was dug in to the hill, and upon the other builded out wards and fortified with rocks. Streams rushed down under it, and some over it. At last at the top we looked back, & only then could we see clearly the whole road we had come, laid upon the mountain like the folds of a filibeg.

We advanced a mile in to the lee of the hill and rested. Now & then we heard in the North short sharp claps of thunder echo'ing off the hill sides. But they were not thunder. The Sky men had heard them the previous year – it was the red coated sodgers breaking down the rocks & precipices with fire-work bombs, at the place where they were still laying the road.

But by the time we descended to their camp they had ceased their labors. We caught sight of them from above, assembled in to six companies, each at ease beside a great fire whereupon they were rosting cattle. The place is call'd the Hollow of Milk, but it was not milk they were drinking. Where our way passed by their camp we met an half dozen of them and ask'd them for what purpose was their feast. They had more drink taken than they coud well hold and they invited us to join them, perhaps, we fear'd, to make sport of us. They told us that it was the birth day of the King and that their leader – this was the same tall Irish man Wade that I had once seen at Strontian – he had given them all half a day's leave and feasting to honour him. They press'd drink upon us for pledging his Health.

'To his Majesty the King in London, may he live long!' they pledged, and watched us closely for our reply. Michael stept forward.

'I will willingly drink to that', said he and he raised his cup, 'May the King live long in London!'

So we came out of the muirs, and turned West in to Glengarry's country. On the second day we reached the head of Loch Hourn, & here Michael and I parted with the Sky men, taking our road past Barrisdale's house and South thorow Knoidart. Thence we found a boat that carry'd us to Mallagveck, where I left Michael.

I thoght to reach home that night, but the wind and rain came on so fiercely that I was forced at last to take shelter by the Morar river, and there I slept. My plaid was wet to the inside, but it kept the wind off me all the better for that and I slept the night without waking. These bones were young in those days!

When I awoke the wind was long gone. I was

lying in a deep dew, and when I rose my form slept on in the grass behind me. The birds were allready at their song, & 'sweet to me was their morning music, after waking from my sleep!' I wrung out my bonnett & was on my way.

I past the silent farm of Bracarina, and climb'd the road above the loch. I coud see Brinacory island ahead. I came round the last brow & saw my glen before me at last, with the loch flat & calm, and our farm & the valley bottom under the Autumn mist silent and still, the smoke from the roofs rising straight, and my hills in their own dawn shadow, & the sky behind them golden.

IV

I marry

That was the end of my wandering. More than sixty years have past since then and never again have I gone out of my country, unless to fish off the shores of it.

My mother's eyes were full of tears & laughter both on my return. She took my plaid and made a smoke fire of bog mirtle to clean it out – she said I coud have got a good price for it in Crief, with all the 'livestock' that was in it. For my part I had some news for her, that I had got from the man to whom I had past the letter: Hugh, Morar's son, was returned from ffrance and had been made a Bishop in Edinburgh, and he was coming north to serve the Highlanders. My friend, the first Bishop for the Highlands, and the first Highland man a Bishop! As my mother fixed her new lamp upon the wall she asked when was I for building my own house & taking a bride in to it? – may be then I would be the first man married by this first Highlander a Bishop! And so in fact it turn'd out, allthow it was not in our mind untill then, Our plan was to marry next Spring, after Lent was over – this woud give me time to gather all that woud be needed for the building of the house, and to build when the land was dry enough.

On every fair day that Autumn I labor'd at the preparations, and my brothers Calum and Donald, & Donald Brinacory's son and the other men of our farm helped me when they could. We chose the place, & first broght to it stones enough for the base of the wall. Near the end of the year we hunted the land for willows, and cut and stored enough sods for walls & roof before the frost woud harden them or the rain make them useless. And for a week

1732 of Winter nights I sat at my mother's fire – and Peggy sat at hers – making pins of heather stems & hazel twig ties for the roofing. The wall posts and roof couples and the main roof tree, & the wooden hinges for the door, I had from the house of my uncle Calum Peter, which had lain empty for the year past after he died. He had promised to leave them to me, years ago when I was a boy.

Easter fell late that year, and within a week of it we were ready to make a start. If I had had the choice of all East & West Brinacory I cou'd not have chosen a fitter place for a house. You can see that yourself. The ground is dry & level, in a good hollow place, close to the path, and in those days it was shelter'd by birch trees. I clear'd the ground and laid the course of stones, large enough for house & byre together, ten good paces long and four wide, and made round at the corners. The gap for the door I faced to the East, away from the wind and all the host of the Dead that ride upon it. Then I went to my bed, for on the morrow the rest of them were to join with me for the building.

The wall posts we set upright and fix'd them firmly at the bottom amidst the course of stones, and then we built the walls of woven willows to the hight of our eye, and bound each to each. The whole thing we builded up on the outside with sods. To the tops of the posts we tied the couples and the beams, on either side, and these again we made secure to the roof tree where they met at the centre. The roof we builded with sods cut thin, starting at the top of the wall & laying each row over the one below, fixing them down with the pins, & with cut ferns sticking out from under them for the thatch. Over all we laid the straightest willow wands that we had saved for this purpose, and made them secure with the hazel wood ties. It was not necessary to hold the roof down with ropes & stones, as some men do, because of the shelter of the place. Once the roof was on all that was left was to make the door, and a wall inside to shoulder hight to divide the house from the byre. The last of the willows we used for these. Our preparations had been right – not too litle nor scarcely a willow wand or sod left unused at the end. Before the sun set on the second day we had the door swinging on its hinges.

That house lasted us ten years before I pull'd it down & builded up an other. I made four alltogether in my life time, every one in this hollow. This last one has done me for thirty years past, but Peggy never sat at the fire of it, may God be mercifull to her.

The first time I saw Bishop Hugh I asked him to marry us, and the date was fix'd for a fortnight after Mayday. Coming up to Easter Peggy and I had walked to Tarbert to speak with her cousin Donald Angus. He made the best whiskey to be had – with the copper pot he used it was far purer than any thing we coud make with the tin pot we had at Brinacory. A few of the farms kept a pot in those days, and the families shared it, but for a wedding they allways went to Donald Angus. A 'black pot' was the name we gave to them, but this one was far from black – it was a perfect new one, just boght, & I am not sure which glow'd brighter, the pot or himself. He told us to come back in four weeks & he would have it ready.

Said he, 'My ram with the curly horn will make you the best whiskey to be tasted this side of the land of ever-lasting youth'.

Two weeks before the date I went the round of my kin and friends to invite them all. Peggy did the same for hers, and we were carefull to avoid each other on these journeys, for good luck's sake. On the last day, on the eve, we had the house bless'd.

We were married in the Chapel on the White Island, the one that had been without a roof when I was there as a boy. I made the walk to it with my mother and my brothers, and as we looked down upon the loch far below we saw the boat of Peggy's father Michael moving like a twig upon it, and Peggy sitting in the back of it. It was a day fit for a wedding and the middle of May. There was not a cloud in the sky, nor scarce a ripple on the water. All who coud walk or crawl were there, gathered on the shore facing the island. It must have taken twenty or thirty boat journeys to get them over, & we had an half dozen boats ready for the job. Donald, Brinacory's son, swam across, as he said 'for the very pleasure of the day'.

Of the Mass, from start to finish, I can remember nothing, only that I had my left brog untied. And of all Bishop Hugh's sermon I can recall only one thing that he said to us, 'Be true to each other'.

Michael left his boat for Peggy and me and whiles the rest made the walk I row'd her back to Swordland. We were in no hurry. We drew the boat up at last as the sun was out over the sea. The trees stood stock still, full of hidden doves and thrushes, and the evening air smelt sweet and warm.

By the time we enter'd her house the meal was allready started. The entire house was set aside for it, for the wall that divided room from byre had been thrown out in the field, and heathers had been laid over the whole floor.

'Eat up', said Catherine – that was Peggy's mother – as we took our places on the bench, 'and never have hunger after!'

She had beef laid down, and mutton & half a dozen capons, & no end of eggs. And a horn of ale coming your way it seem'd between each mouthful! Out side Donald Bracarina was tuning his pipes, passing to and fro across the door – the drones were like twin lambs without a mother to him, for all the

care he took with them. When at last he deign'd
to make a start Peggy and I were piped out of the
house and pointed West, and then we left them all
to it, young and old, to dance reels, the boys to
wrastle and the youngest to fall asleep against the
house end. A crescent moon came up and shadows
fill'd the hollows.

I walk'd her the road we knew well and broght
her to our home. Three times I walk'd her round
it, sun-wise, and then I took her in. There were
sticks and peats left ready and with these she lit her
fire. You cou'd not find fault with her. With care
she lit it, and never in all the years did she let it out
and need to borrow a lit peat to her shame, though
many was the morning that an other came to ask
fire out of her house.

She had broght Columba's herb to hang over the
door, and she had made a cross of straws that she
set in the room upon the end wall. She put a turf in
the window, and swept the floor from the corners
out to the door. She fix'd the cross again, straighter.
She smothered the fire, and tidied about it, and
gave an other sweep to the floor. She re-arranged
a pot or two. She said her prayer over by the cross.
And then she turn'd to me. And then I broght my
virgin bride to bed.

On the morrow, as was the custom, her mother
was the first to visit us, and she took the snood from
Peggy's head and fix'd the kerch upon her. Then
my mother & Michael came in together, she with
the gift of a pot for dy'ing and my father's wooden

cup with the writing on it, and the crusie lamp from Crieff which she had allways intended for us. And after them came all our kin & friends who had presents to give. Peggy fill'd her home that day, between bowls and spoons, kerchiefs and blankets & a checkr'd plaid. And then, as the custom is yet, we our selves served a good meal to those who had served us. And so the day went in. But she and I were not holding back on the drinking this time, and (speaking for my self) I do not entirely recall the ending of it.

Betwixt what I had saved and what Peggy broght for her dowry, we began our life together well provided. We had all our oats sown, and enough of the best grain kept back to last us the year round. I had two milch cows and their followers, & half a dozen goats and a couple of horses on the hill, & Peggy had as many sheeps.

The wedding was scarcely come & gone before I had the peats to cut, and then away to the Shielding to mend the walls and roof of our hutts there ready for the women coming up. It was high up beyond the Mass Stone, where the Priest's Burn is barely a stream, on a sloping patch of green under the clifts. The grass is rich there, and to the cattle's liking.

On the longest day of Summer we broght them up – milch cows, stirks and hiefers. All the women of the farm came, and the children running ahead, each with some thing to carry, whether blanket, pot or churn. From up at the hutts I heard them coming, for the boys driving the beasts made sure that the world would hear the halloos of them, and as I went down for an other load I past the women, bent back'd, singing as they climb'd, and their song was 'Out at the shieldings of the hill'. One was leading a horse that bore a creel on either side, and in one her infant was tied, whiles in the other was set a stone to ballance him.

We had a small hut for churning and storing butter and cheese, and two larger ones for sleeping in and retiring to when once the chill of evening descended on the land. There were turves set about the fire for the women to sit upon, and they had great nights of it with songs and stories, and treats for the children on special days – a gallon of croudie on St Peter & Paul's day, and on the ffeast of St Michael a bannock near as big as a quern with an angel mark'd upon it – 'St Michael's Shield' we called it. Thorow the day Peggy woud be cutting fleeces and washing & dy'ing them, & making the butter and cheese, & the girls & boys woud be herding the beasts. Every one loved those weeks up on the hill – as my mother used to say, 'If you are young the sun allways shines at the shielding'.

As to myself, I was more down at the farm than on the hill. The corn was to be cut, after the new moon of September, and it had to be broght in as soon as I had it cut. Peggy came down for a day to get it in the quicker. She gather'd it in the Swordland manner, pulling it up root and stalk together and separating the grains in the ashes of a fire with a stick. Many wou'd laugh this to scorn these days, but that was her father Michael's way of doing it. Any way, between us we gather'd all that I had sown, leaving only the last root growing to bring good fortune to our marriage.

That first year I had four riggs of good ground under oats, but my intention was to sow at least a couple every year, even the years when I woud be sowing bere, because I had agreed with Brinacory to pay him one quarter Boll of oats as part of our year's rent, as well as such hens, eggs & cheese as we could spare, with peats in the dry years. I was also to cut oak wood for him each Winter, and bring it up the loch to Tarbert, as part of the rent, keeping for our own fire whatever dead timber I might gather. What we coud not pay by these means was to be paid in money.

It was a fortnight after All Saints' day, with a snell cutting wind from off the mountains, and I had come in to dig clean the floor of the byre (as we allways did at this time of the year, and again in the Spring), when Peggy call'd over to me from the fire. I threw down the spaid and stood with my elbows on the wall, and she came across to me and gave me the news that she was with child. Her eyes were shining; she had been waiting all day to tell me.

'But you will need to see to the door and the roof both', she said when I had come round to sit beside her. 'Thank God it will be a Spring child and have the Summer sun, & be strong on my breast before next Winter is in. I never fear'd the Winter before, Ian, but I fear it now, with a child to be in the house. And I fear when the meal barrell is empty, and we must drink the blood of the cattle, & keep alight the fire with their dung when the peats are wasted.'

1733   Allmost from the first Peggy had no hesitation that our child woud be a daughter. And so it happened. She was born a week after May morning, the easiest first child that ever slipt out in to the world, and she was baptised by Bishop Hugh in our own house, and given the name Mary, whose month she was born in. And so we went in to the second year of our marriage. 'The first is the year of kisses, the second is the year of blows', so the proverb says, but there were never blows betwixt us, not in the second year, nor the third, nor in all our years.

V

Bishop Hugh & Mr William

Hugh stayed on the White Island and was our priest as well as our Bishop. Because we had been friends as boys he told me things that perhaps he told to few others. He knew they would not go beyond me: some I have never spoken of to any man untill today.

He said to me that just after he himself became a priest Bishop James had beg'd the men in Rome to give us our own bishop for the Highlands. He was growing too old himself for journeying; he saw how his people were hunted by the Lowland sodgers, though we in the West were shelter'd from them by the mountains & the sea; & he knew that many were being lost and others who might have been baptised were not, all for want of a Bishop who had our language. When at last he got his wish he chose a priest call'd Mr Alexander John & sent him away to be consecrated. I believe this man got the length of Rome, but he was never made a Bishop, why I do not know. And after that he disappear'd from sight & they say he died in that country. Anyway, that left Bishop James with an other choice to make, and so it was that Hugh was chosen, allthough he was little more than thirty and only six years a priest. It was a good choice, even so.

His family were known to us all, & he himself was loved for the man he was. When he learned that he had been chosen, that was when he had ask'd to be sent a while to ffrance, because he had no experience of the world beyond the mountains.

Untill he had the chance to see things for him self he had thoght that all was well every where in the Highlands, having 'till then only been among his own people. Now he saw (as he expressed it) how few were the laborers to bring in the harvest, & he at once made up his mind, first & above all else, to get priests for his people. But they must be Highland men, who woud think as a Highland man thinks & speak as a Highland man speaks, for too often outsiders had come & gone, or grown old whiles still young amoung our muirs & mists. And they would get their training here too, for (as he said) all the learning in the Colleges of Paris & Rome will not haul a man up a clift nor bring him home over the sea in a black storm.

So it was that he open'd his door on the White Island again, for boys to study to be priests there. It needed an other house to be built, & the men of Buorblach and Beoraid builded it for him, at the very time that I was building my own house. Money was needed allso, & some came, thank God, from Bishop James who had a love for that house since he it was who had made our first school there. Nor did our old master Mr George forget that Hugh had been his pupil, & it was thorow his good word that money was sent from Paris. And so the school was opened the month after Peggy and I were married.

Bishop Hugh gave the boys his own books to use, & had others sent from Edenburgh. The Library that he made for them he show'd me, & I counted more than two hundred books in it. But it was not alone books that he gave those boys − every day he gave them his time, and his strength. And that was the way it was with all his bishop's work. He never spared him self, allthough he had not been strong since a boy. Many the man warn'd him of the early grave, but he only laughed. And their warnings very nearly came true. The third Winter he was amoung us was a bad one; it carried off two children from Swordland, and many cattle up and down the loch, & it nearly carried off Hugh. He lay in his bed from Christmas untill Easter, & the woman who tended him would peep in each morning and bend down to listen if he was dead yet, so low was he. But if anyone was counting on him dying they were disappointed, for he lived close on an other forty years. 1734

It was the day after Palm Sunday when he at last got out of his bed, & that was to baptise our second child. We gave him the name Ian, after myself, and Ian Beg he was known as. And a year later Hugh return'd to baptise our third, that was Michael, who was named for Peggy's father. But he died of the Sickness when he was just starting to talk. There is no need to ask God to be mercifull to him. Peggy hardly ever spoke about him afterwards, except a 1735 few times to me, but I know that not a day in her life went by that she was not sighing for him.

1737   It was about that time that the school was taken off the White Island. Hugh's brother John was in those days the tacksman of Guidale farm, which is only a few miles distant to the South, and he had a new built house there, one of the first builded of stone they say. It was there that Hugh put the boys for their school. His own sister's son John became one of the scholars, & this John went on to become a priest, & later a Bishop to help Hugh, & in the end he took the place of Hugh himself

After the boys left the White Island Hugh stay'd there on his own, & every Summer he broght all his priests there to meet together, or as many as could make the journey. Altogether the island was his home for fifteen years, that is when he was at home. But more often than not he was away over the mountains, or out to the islands, & then we were left without a priest. And it was for that reason that as soon as he had the chance he gave us Mr William.

Harrison, that was this Mr William's English name, & he came from the East where his father had land. He had a brother a monk in Germany, and he had himself done some of his studying in that country, allthough he was ordain'd in Rome. He was a learned man – he some times call'd himself 'Doctor' – & he could write in Latin & Italian. He did not have our language when he first came to us.

Where he had lived as a boy they spoke it litle (&
even that was coarse), but he had forgotten what-
soever he once had, so that at first he spoke nought
but English & I was one of the only ones he cou'd
speak to. That is how I know all these things. Most
often I was the one who woud explain his words to
our neighbours. What they did for Confession I am
not certain! But I know of some who allways waited untill Bishop Hugh was away so that they woud
be sure to get Mr William, because many a sin slipt
by without his understanding that they might have
blush'd to face Hugh with. Any way, as time went
by he began to master our language, allthough at
first he did not stray far beyond 'It is wet today',
& for many mounths he woud be making daily
announcements about the weather, so that some of
the boys took to calling him 'Mr Wet-Today'.

Bishop Hugh made him the priest for Morar's
Morar allso, & he had to get across there as best he
coud. The first Summer he used our farm's currach   1738
if ever he wanted over to Mewboll. But he never
master'd it or learned to make it go straight. One
day Hugh & I met him as he was struggling to get
the thing to the shore.

'Our Lord rode in to Jerusalem on a donkey', said
Hugh to me out loud and in English so as to be
heard by him, 'but our Mr William rowed in to
Mewboll on a mule!'

'And he took the round about route', said I.

Hugh used to tease him, because he liked to keep
up his dignity. Any way, as soon as possible we

builded a pointed boat for him, one that he could handle.

I know he found the life in our country hard to endure – he confided this to me many years later.

'When I first came here', he told me, 'I many times wished I had never taken the Mission oath. I saw clearly that to be here meant to deny myself for ever the comforts of life, & the esteem & wealth that my family were used to & that with my education I might have expected. I even harbor'd the hope of becoming a Jesuit, so that I coud serve in a wealthy house amoung polished people. But when I went to our Bishop for counsel he shewed me that the vanities I coveted – comfort & esteem & wealth – were the very temptations of our Saviour in the desert'.

'If this is your desert', he said to me, 'remember that you bring manna to our people here, without which they must starve. There are places where some are starving & falling away, & where others are hungry to receive the ffaith but can not, only for want of a priest'.

'After that I pray'd daily to turn my back on those temptations. And slowly I put every trace of regret behind me, untill now there is no where on earth I woud sooner be than here in Glengarry's Morar.'

It was a hard life he had here, all the same. Not for him a hutt of his own to stay in, as you have now. He lived from day to day in one man's house or an other, & I believe none of them was like the house he was raised in, where no one stoopt thorow the door. The people fed him, & even cloath'd him, as he journey'd to and fro the length of the loch or across the hills. Word would run ahead of him of the road he was taking, & we woud watch for him coming over the hill. We were looking out for a litle man leading a horse with a fat belly & a basket swinging on either side of it. One basket had his needs for life in it, & the other his needs for the Mass. We thoght it a blessing if he slept at our home, and often we woud contend one with an other as to who should have him. There were a few, then as now, right enough, that woud grudge the very shell of their egg to any man, even a priest; but they are not worth the wasting of your ink on them.

The first Spring he came here I mind he was visiting our farm, & he stay'd in my mother's house. She told me he seem'd ill at ease, & she wondered was he displeased with her hospitality. But when I spoke to him, & worked round to the subject, it turn'd out that he was plagued with worry as to whether or not he had said the Easter Mass on the right Sunday. Bishop Hugh was out of the country, I think in Moidart, & there was no way for Mr William to know the date of the feast for certain. He said he had sent word by letter to Bishop James in Edinburgh asking him to post a book back to him (an 'Almanack' he call'd it), so that he coud find out if he had been in the right.

It was the people of Bracarina farm who made his Communion hosts, just as they do for you still.

They have a bit of land down there where the earth is good & the wheat plant will grow on it. They sow a small patch there every year, & make breads enough to last the year round. I do not know when this started, or how the seeds were first broght there. My father told me it was an Irish man had them broght in on a vessell, & he did it because before that time you had to send as far as the Low Country for wheaten hosts, & you might be waiting half the Winter for them.

I must tell you allso the story of Mr William's chasuble. It was a fine white one that he came to us with. But one time he was staying the night in the house of an old cottager over in Glasnacardoch, & he had it spred out as he allways did so that no creases woud come in it, when two cocks suddenly began a fight amoung the ashes. And before any one cou'd kick them out they had the ashes over the vestment, & a morsell of smoldering peat put a large burn mark on the white, just by the cross at the back where every one coud see it. They had one of the cocks for dinner the next day, but the other they could not catch. Mr William had to use a woven cloke untill he coud get a real chasuble. But he was a man who liked every thing to be just right. Any way, he arranged it that a man over at Tarbert was to ask of any Vessell that call'd there, did they carry any cloth of the kind he needed? And late that Summer a big ship came in from a foreign land, & she was carrying silks. I think Morar must have given Mr William money, because he was off up the road to Tarbert at a run as soon as he heard about it, & he came back with a large piece of white & a smaller piece of gold. He call'd them 'Brocade'. The white piece had flowers of red & blue & green done in thred upon it. Morar's wife had the knowledge of working with a needle, and she it was who made his Chasuble. It was the finest you coud ever imagine, with the cross & the edges in gold, The children loved to feel it with their fingers, & they used to ask him to turn it to and fro to catch the sun.

Every year before Christmas and Easter he heard the people's Confession, as best he coud that is. At Christmas this was allways done in a house, but at Easter it was outside if possible. There were four places for Confession in Glengarry's Morar. Beoraid by the foot of the loch was allways the first, & he stay'd there a day or two. Then Mallegvore the same, then Tarbert, & last Swordland. The whole thing took about a week. He himself woud get his own Confession from Bishop Hugh if he was in our country. But some of the priests in the islands had no way to get it, except when they all came together for their meetings on the loch, & if ever one could not travel for sickness or bad weather he might be two or even three years without Confession.

As the years past & Mr William grew more at his ease amoung us, and more a master of our language, so we grew more at our ease with him. We willingly took our questions and our quarrells to him,

& he made judgement on our disputes, unless it was some great matter that needed to be taken to Glengarry. But pity you if you went to him when you were in the wrong, for he was a fiery litle man & more than one man he beat up the road with his hands over his ears for protection. He did not miss you and hit the house wall, as they say. He was honest & straight, and if he had his faults, as we all do surely, he served our needs off & on for thirty and five years – he went away but came back to us, you see, & that is a story in itself that I must tell you about an other day.

His first stay here was maybe seven years, and one of the last things he did was to bury my good mother. She was close on seventy when she died, & she went with no pain, in her own house, with her sons at her side. May God be mercifull to her, & to my father.

1744

Soon afterwards Mr William was taken out of our country, and the date is easily remember'd, for it was just a few mounths before the coming of our Prince.

VI

The coming and the going of the Prince

Of the year of the Prince, & his battles, I can not
tell you much. I believe you will know more
about it than I, because all I know is what others
have told me. But I can tell you of some things that
happened afterwards in our own country, which it
may be you have not heard.

Bishop Hugh often spoke of how it happened that
he was one of the first to hear that our Prince had
landed. He was returning from Edenburgh by the
Western road and met up with his kinsman Donald
of Kin Loch Moideart, & it was from his mouth he
heard the news. He pursued his way home wards
by the coast of Arasaig untill he found the ffrench
vessell at anchor, & in it the Prince in the clothing
of a Priest. Hugh pled with him to sail away at once,
and to wait a year untill the Chiefs woud be ready,
& others pled the same. But he woud not be moved,
so warm was he to claim his father's right there &
then. So at the last & against their will the chiefs
broght out their men. Some broght them out them
selves; others sent them out with their sons to lead
them; some to their great shame found excuses to
send none. And when the first ones gathered upon
the hill above the ffinna river on the land of Glena-
ladale Hugh was there to bless their banner.

1745

Glengarry's people have always answer'd the call to arms of the true King. Dark Alister led us at Killiecrankie, before I was ever born, & he saw his own son Donald fall there after killing eighteen they say. And the same Alister broght five hundred to Sherrif Muir when I was a boy. But this time (it is said) seven hundred came out for the young Prince. Glengarry's son Aeneas led them, untill he was killed within the year, before he reached the age of twenty, not in battle but by a ball fired by accident. Most of those who went with him came from East of the mountains, but there were some also from Knoidart, & most of the farms in our own country sent at least one man. All these were led by Colla of Barrisdale & young Scotus – Donald of the Glen as we all called him – & one of the officers who went with them was my friend Donald, Brinacory's son.

There were men out from Morar's Morar allso, and some of them were known to us. Michaelina's man's brother was one. They were the first of any men to join the Prince. Morar's brother John led them, & Mr Alan – the same Uist man Alan who was sent to Rome from the White Island – he went as their priest and was made the Prince's own Chaplain. They say you woud not have known him for a priest unless he was saying the Mass or giving the Blessing, for he fought in the plaid & the white cockade just like the other Gentlemen.

Our own people did not head for Glen Finnan. Their plan was to gather at Tarbert, & cross over in to Glen Dessary in order to meet up with the Prince further in the East. On the day they were to set out everyone from youngest to oldest left the cattle & came down from the shieldings and made their way to Tarbert to watch them go. There Mr Aeneas climb'd in to a boat, drawn up upon the shingles, and gave them a Blessing as they stood upon the flat meadow – a Blessing for the men who were going, & one for the families who woud be waiting for them. And at the end of it they raised their weapons in a halloo, so that the sun danced upon them, & the crowd prest close about and answer'd the shout. Then up they went round the shoulder of the hill above the loch, with the dust rising off the road about them. And after they were past the crags & out of sight, three or four more halloos, each one more far off, came to the ears of those upon the shore & were answer'd by them.

All this was told to me afterwards. I did not see it myself, for I was in our house, or pacing at the door of it. Peggy was ready to give birth to our sixth child at any time; & she knew that all was not well. It was five days before she gave birth at last, & the infant was still born. She was a beautiful, perfect, dark haired girl, and I buried her a little below on the bank, though there was scarcely time to do it for Peggy her self was near to dying in the house. Old Catherine & Mary Angus were tending her, and with the help of Christ & His holy Mother & St Ann they kept her alive. Peggy was allways strong and that saved her, but she was three weeks in her bed, & a mounth before she stir'd beyond the door. By that time our Prince was at the gates of Edenburgh, so the question should I go with him? was answer'd – my place was to be at home.

Allthough Peggy was growing stronger, every day her sadness seemed to grow more sharp. She did not go up to the shielding at Michaelmass to bring our neighbours down. She cou'd not lift her spirit, & I was unable to help her, much tho' I tried to. And then soon after that the Winter was upon us, when the world it self lay dead around her. It was a Winter of frosts and snell winds that

1746   never ended. Christmas & the New Year came, & then February crept by, & after it a March of black skies. And when at the last we got to April & I was praying that Spring would not be long coming to lift her, there came to us the news from Culloden Muir, & suddenly our home – and all the country about us – was stunned as if by an other death.

Let me tell you how we got the news. It was three days after it happened, with no word come to the West of any battle fought or lost, & I was fishing on the loch, knowing nothing of it. By mid morning I was drifted beyond Srone Vore & I thoght to take the chance of calling on Peggy's sister at Kinloch to give her word of Peggy's health. But when I reached her house her husband James and the boys were out on the hill searching for one of their milch cows that had stray'd there looking for the company of the heifers. I sett out to join them, & so it was that

I found my self up beyond the head of the farm &
across the boundary stream upon the hill grazing
above Oban. I had hardly planned when I set out
from home to be in Morar's country that day, but
that is where I was. I was searching in below a clift
when I came upon three men resting there. I took
them to be men of Oban farm & I asked them had
they seen the cow. They did not answer at once, &
seem'd to be looking me up & down, as if making up their minds about me. Only when James
came by driving the beast before him were they
put at their ease. He knew at once that they were
not men of Oban but strangers in the country, &
he enquired as to their home and where they were
headed. They had been out with the Prince, they
told us, & had come alive off Culloden Muir, and
were bound for Mewboll and then home to Sky.
The army was scatter'd, and the Prince they supposed was in hiding some where. Once they could
see by our faces which side we stood for they spoke
more freely and told us all that had happen'd after
the army had returned out of England. They said
that since the battle the country in the East was full
of spies.

While we were thus talking one of them caught
sight of a figure on the hill, moving forward towards
us amoung the rocks. They were minded to keep
out of sight of strangers, so we all prest together
against the clift, keeping silent untill he woud pass
us by. But as he climbed down he turned & caught
sight of us. James at once leapt out & held him. And

now we could see that he was just a boy; he might not have been more than fifteen.

And then there was a strange scene. The oldest of the men stept forward. The boy at once embraced him, & then turned and kiss'd the hand of the youngest. It seems that he was the oldest man's son, & a scholar in the town of Inverness. Malcolm was his name. When word of the Battle had come to the town he had slipt out of the school, & got him self a targe, sword & dagger, and hasten'd to the field to play what part he coud. He told us how he only reached the edge of the battle, for allready when he arrived the lines were broken & the enemy victorious. But he was certain he had caught sight of his father in the distance, and when at last he got safe off the field he had headed West in the hope of finding him, for he judged he wou'd be making for Sky. He had hidden his targe & sword, but his dagger he still had with him,

James prest them to come down to his house to eat & rest, but they were for staying clear of farm towns, even here in the West. So he led them to a Shielding hutt just below the hill, and pointed out the mouth of the Mewboll river to them & then we left them to rest before they woud continue their journey.

The hills and the loch had no pleasure for me as I returned home that day. My mind was full of our army in flight, and our Prince somewhere in hiding, and men skulking at that very moment amoung the mountains, & boys too, perhaps, like Malcolm.

When I thoght of him my heart wrung with pity,
for I do not think I ever saw such courage, modesty
& gaiety together in a lad. What woud become of
them all, I wonder'd.

Well, we heard some time later that father & son
were afterwards taken by the red sodgers, & put
upon a Vessell bound for London. There were hundreds of good men with them in the hold of that
ship, lying upon gravell with their food thrown
down amoung them like dogs in a pit, & many died
before ever the voyage was ended. But Malcolm
and his father lived. They were sent to a prison ship
anchor'd upon the London river, & there they lay
for mounths, at the door of death, with the stink of
dead & dying men around them. But they got home
to Sky at the last, and lived in happiness there.

And that was how the news of Culloden came to
us – bit by bit. Michaelina's man's brother returned
in a week or two, & now we were waiting most of
all for the return of Donald, Brinacory's son, or for
word of him. But he never came home, and at last
we learned that he had died upon the field. I was
told by one who saw it that he got a bad wound
from a ball in the stomack, & was lying there an
hour or more. And after the battle he was trying
to creep to the edge of the field, but one of the red
sodgers who had been sent amoung the wounded
saw him moving and cut his throat.

That was not the worst they did after the battle. We
heard of a young man, Angus, from Lettermorar,

whom they burnt alive inside a house where he had crept with others for safety. And it was not long before they came across in to our country to take their revenge wherever. A ship was sent to our coast – the ffurnace it was called, and a man fferguson was its captain. I should better say 'Beast' than 'Man'. I have never seen the Power of Evil so certainly in a man's eyes as I saw it in his. Everywhere he went he punished and flogged whomsoever he coud catch – you can find more than one man walking these glens yet who carries the scratches of fferguson's Cat upon his back.

This day just after May morning we got word that he was burning Colla of Barrisdale's House over at Inverie. We ran round to Tarbert to catch sight of it, along with a hundred others from the farms along the road. It was a great House of many chambers, new built out of stones & lime, & it had a roof of black slates. There was not an other house any thing like it in Knoidart. We watched the black feather of smoke rise up & hover & spread above it, far away across the loch, and now & then we coud even catch the smell of it upon the breeze.

A week later they burnt Morar's house down at Cross the same, and again we went to witness it. I was standing amoung the crowd watching the roof cave in when the one standing beside me tap'd me upon the shoulder. I turned, & I knew him without hesitation. It was the school master Alexander, the poet, who had saved me at the mine of Strontian. As we stept back from the heat he told me his news.

He had met the Prince when first he landed, and was made his Officer to lead the men of Ardnamurchan. He had gone with him in every battle to the last one.

'We had no chance at Culloden', he said with bitterness. 'We were sent out on half an hour's sleep & a bisket.'

Now he was a fugitive. His house had been ruined. His wife and son & daughter, & three more girls born since we last met, he had not seen for a month past. He meant to reach them as soon as he could, & take them out of Clanranald's countrey.

'May the Blessed Trinity keep them safe from our enemies till then!' said he, crossing him self, & then he laughed out loud for he caught sight of the look on my face.

'Yes, I came over to the True ffaith a year ago', he told me, 'and that was how I had to give up the school'.

I took him to stay at our home, & he met Peggy. I told her that this was the bard whose songs were the equal of my own, & he there and then made some verses for her in praise of Morar, which I believe he afterwards put in his Book. I was glad to have him in our house — it raised Peggy's spirit. There was allways either laughter or brawling wheresoever he went. And I was glad also for the chance to give him hospitality.

'I have been all these years in your debt', I said to him, 'and I have allways had it in mind to repay you.'

'You repaid me on the road to finnan Island, allthogh you did not know it', he replied, 'for you sowed a seed in my head that day that lay some years & then began to grow.'

Alexander had been upon the island of Eigg & he had seen with his own eyes what fferguson had done there, leaving the place without bull or cow and with scarce a man. Two score of the young men he had rounded up like animals, & dragged them off the land to be sent to London & there sold for slaves in the Indies. Many left wives & children behind, without so much as the chance of a farewell. Not one ever returned.

After that the ffurnace had sailed on to Cannay, & put the people in fear of their lives there. The sailors took a woman who was carrying her child eight months, & were awaiting their chance to ravish her, whatever her condition. But she guessing their intention escaped from the hutt they were holding her in & hid the night in a bog where best she coud. But the cold & the struggle and the terror broght on her birth, & she and her infant died both.

For sure, Cruelty & Torture were the thing that this fferguson and his men knew best. And it was thorow torture that they allmost captured Bishop Hugh. This is how it happened. Hugh had returned to the White Island that Spring, and his brother Morar had joined him there soon after his own house was burnt. There were a few others with him allso. McHimmie was there, whose son had broght out six hundred men – he had come on foot over the mountains after the battle, for all his eighty years. They were meeting to decide if there was any way to gather some remains of the army & make a stand amoung the hills. They had taken care that no enemies or spies should get near them, by having all the boats at the foot of the loch broght to the island or kept hidden, for they knew that the ffurnace was at anchor off Arasaig. But it seems that some one there was held & put to torture by fferguson, & he let slip that the Chief & the Gentlemen were met on the island. The sodgers were at once order'd there, and when they discovered that there were no boats to be had they went back & broght two of their own boats up the Morar river as far as it was possible to row. When they reached the rapids they turned them up side down & carried them over the land to the loch, about a dozen men to each boat & the rest swarming round, like red ants carrying away a pair of beetles.

Of course Hugh & the other gendemen had been watching them from the first & they coud see that their hiding place was discovered. So as soon as the sodgers went back to fetch their boats up they themselves rowed over to the South shore, as quickly as they were able, for it was broad daylight. And from there they headed up the loch side on foot.

Morar had a man with him on the island, by name of Angus John, from the farm of Trigh, who was a servant to him. This man they left behind,

with the instruction that he was to gather whatever of Hugh's possessions he could, & in especial
his sacred things & his books, & if chance allowed
bring them off the island in a boat. But he had no
time to do it. Even whiles he was still making a pile
of them the sodgers arrived carrying their boats,
& at the last moment he got himself over to Middle Island. It must be two furlongs, but he swam
across anyway, rather than take a boat that might
betray his whereabouts, and the White Island itself
hid him from view of the sodgers as he swam.
Then he lay under the heather and watched the
sodgers come over to the White Island & search
every inch of it. Of course they found the birds
flown, but signs enough that the nest was not long
empty. So they left a small guard there and the rest
returned to their vessell. Angus John waited untill
night & then swam to the Glengarry shore. But
any thoght of getting home to Trigh he had to put
aside. Instead he headed East. It was close to the
longest day of the year and there was already the
first light of morning in the sky as he was on the
path throrow our farm. So he rested in a bush, &
when the cock crew and the farm began to waken
he came out, & we took him in. And so we got the
news that Hugh had been discovered, but had got
safe away.

But that was not the end of it, & we had not long
to wait for more. That same morning hundreds of
sodgers, the whole nest of them it must have been,
coud be seen by their red coats & the flash of their

weapons, across the loch, moving into Lettermorar.
It was easy to see that they were searching by the
way they stopt & spred out here & there. And then
an hour later suddenly more than a hundred others
came at a trot over the hill above West Brinacory.
Some went hurrying on East; others stopt at our
farm. But they must have known that a hundred
Hughs, & two hundred McHimmies, cou'd easily
stay hid from them. They poked with their fusiles
into the peat stacks, but with only half a heart. They
looked inside our doors, and went into a couple of
houses, and they pulled three or four women out
to question them. Old Catherine was one, and she
was quaking with fear, because Angus John was sitting at that very moment at her hearth. The sodgers
were talking and cursing in their own language,
but she understood not a word. They tried to make
their meaning clear to her by signs, but she only
shook her head & held up her palms to them. Then
one of them scoop'd up some Dung from her house
end & held it above her milk barrell. Still the head
shook. So he dropt the dung slowly into the milk.
Now I can tell you, that was something he was
better not to have done! At once her fear turned to
fury, and she ran at him, spitting & trying to bite
him. He soght to keep her off, & was holding her at
his arms' length up in the air, still swinging up her
legs & trying to land kicks on him, and whatever
she was saying I believe you will not be putting it
in your Book. Then her dog leapt at him, and the
other dogs of the farm join'd the battle, and the

hens flew up out of the thatch. We were sure they were going to put a pike thru her. But they let her go, as you woud let go a wild cat, & kicked the dogs away. I think they might have fired her house & ruined our farm then. But the one in charge of them was keeping a look out with a spy glass over the water, & he saw that those on the South shore were returning down the loch. He perhaps understood by this that they had found what they were looking for. Any way, he order'd his own men to return to their vessell, & off they went; & a while afterwards the rest came by from the direction of Swordland, & disappear'd without harming us. We saw no more of them in our farm after that, because they now knew that the men they sought were on the South side, & that was where they swarm'd for the next three days.

Well, we got word later that they had caught one of them on that first day, just as we guessed. But Hugh and his brother got safely to Mewboll, & from there Hugh got secretly away to Moideart, & after that to ffrance. But the sodgers must have known there was more in hiding, and sure enough on the fourth day they got McHimmie. Some say they found him hiding in a tree; others say that he gave himself up to them. He was too old & sick to go further.

fferguson was pleased enough to have netted the big fish, but his pleasure was less than his anger that two other good sized ones had got away. And so that Hugh might never return to live on the White

Island, he sent a party of his men to destroy the house there. The job was quickly done. No one wou'd have known about it at all, but that two men from Beoraid happen'd to be near to the shore facing across to the Island, & they heard the shouting & cursing. Approaching closer they spied a sodger dancing & cavorting on the rocks drest in a priest's Chasuble. In a couple of hours they were gone, & at once the men took a boat across to see what had been done. They found the whole place ruined. The sodgers had used the pile that Angus John had made to start a fire, and on to it they had thrown the altar of the chapel and all Hugh's books. Most of the books were reduced to ashes; a few were just still recognisable, & one was lying whole although charred at the edges. This one was saved, & kept for Hugh in case he shou'd ever return. Of the holy vestments there was not a trace – they must have gone upon the fire. And any thing the sodgers could not burn they must have carried away, for not a sign remain'd of house or habitation but the blacken'd stones that lay along the base of the wall.

Many went over to see it; but not I. I knew it too well. I had lived in it, & been married in it, & even helped to build part of it. I had no heart to see the ashes of it.

All that Summer we saw nothing but sodgers on the land, & vessells in the Sound. All of them were hunting for the one man. A score of 'Princes' were captured during those days, but the Prince

that matter'd most was not captured: the Prince of
Disguises they never found. We had learned in the
Spring that he was allready safe off the Continent
and lying low in the Hebride Islands, waiting for a
ship to take him to ffrance. And after that we heard
nothing for a long time, except rumors in plenty.
But about a mounth after the capture of McHimmie we had good word that he had returned out of
Sky into Glengarry's Morar, & had come to land on
the rocks by Mallegvore, & from there crossed the
Morar river and headed into Clanranald's country.
And then a week or two after that I got word from
Calum, my sister Michaelina's man, to come across
to Mewboll. When I got there he shewed me the
place where Bishop Hugh & Morar had lain hid
before making their escape. It was a perfect place
for a refuge, hidden amoung rocks & trees so as to
be invisible from above and below. It was hardly to
be reached from below, but was easy to escape from
up in to the hill. It was not too far distant from
the farm town; it had a stream close at hand; and
it looked over the glen both ways. Calum told me
that they were to prepare it for the Prince, for it had
been secretly arranged that he wou'd come there
upon the morrow, & the red sodgers might hunt all
Summer, Autumn & Winter, and the Spring after
it, and they wou'd never find him there.

We spent the rest of the day making it fit for him.
We broght blanketts up, and laid heathers & ferns
on the floor. We put in a bench and a table, with
three or four wooden cups & plates, and a knife for

his meat, & we fixt a woven cross upon the wall. At the cock crow on the morn we were up on the hill laying straight the ground about the place, so that no one could know men had been there. Then three of us went some way distant & sat upon rocks to keep a look out up & down the glen for enemies approaching. Well, I sat a good while thus, and so it was that when next I returned to the hiding place, the Prince was allready there.

There were four or five men with him, as well as our own men, all gathered round him, so that any one could tell at once which one was he. He himself was sitting on the bench, cleaning his knee with the corner of his plaid, & he was busily engaged in it so that his head was lower'd and his face hid. Then he looked up.

His brain was quicker than my own.

'Well met, for a second time!' he cried to me with a laugh, whiles I was still saying to myself, 'I have seen you before some where'. Then betwixt the face & the voice I knew him; it was the same man whose hand Malcolm had kissed upon the hill. Yes, the same face, but yet so changed from that face of three months before. Now with a red beard, and hair longer & un-cared for. A common man of the Highlands he seem'd but yet with a Nobility that still shone out in his eye. It was as if I was looking at a picture of a Prince, dirtied & soiled.

And his face was changed in an other way too. He was the heartiest in the company, for sure, but that very laughter in his eyes seem'd somehow a forced, brave gaiety.

'This is the finest house I have had to sleep in since the Palace of Holy Rood!' he cried, looking over our handiwork. 'I have had many landlords since then, God knows. Do you know, in my last house I could touch both the walls at once with my elbows! But I have enjoyed the best of company too. Some nights even, boys, Betty Burke slept in my bed! And I have learned many a new thing that I woud never have learned at the Court. I know how to stand upright amoung the smoke under a roof beam without choking – I wager not an other Prince of Europe cou'd do it. And I have learned how to live content in the company of lice. For you see, Gentlemen, I travel with a large Retinue! The lice have got closer to me than ever the Red Coats have, for sure! And so have the midges!' he added, slapping at his face. And then he lit up a clay pipe he carried.

'This is some thing else I have learned in my skulking', he said, smiling round us.

He ate & drank then, his fill. And after a cup or two of wine he began to sing, softly so not to draw attention to his hiding place. I recall well the song he sang – 'The King Shall Enjoy His Own Again'; and yet I believe that he allready knew in his heart there woud be no climbing back from Culloden.

Strange were my thoghts as I watched him. Awe & pity both I felt for him; the pity the more because of his courage, & the awe the greater for the pity. And you know, whiles I was tending to his wants, if

I chanced to brush against him, it was like touching the hem of Our Lord, or of His angel. God forgive me if that is Blasphemy to say; but then did not a star rise at his birth?

He was no more than two hours in our company, when urgent word came that sodgers were gather'd by the coast, & were heading inland. Some urged that he woud be safest to bide where he was, but others feared that somehow word of his whereabouts might have got to the enemy, & he must leave the place. And in the end that was what was agreed. In haste he bade us ffarewell, & thanked us, promising to return. And then he set out towards the East, with three of those who had come with him.

A mounth after that we heard from one of those who had accompanied him that he was in the West again, close to where he had first landed, & that ffrench ships were lying at anchor, ready to get him away. And that is how it happened. He sailed into his exile. And so he left us, in a worse state than he found us. He left us a harvest of young widows.

I have told you about some of those widows in our own country who lost their men, killed on the field or snatch'd from their homes. Now I will tell you a tale with a happy ending, of a man who did return, all though only just. You must know Donald Peter Angus who lives with his daughter over at Stouil. Well, it is his story, & one day you should ask him to tell you the details of it, for just about every thing happened to him that cou'd happen to a man who follow'd our Prince. I only know the bones of it.

He must have been about twenty and four years old then, and married for a year, with a babe new born – that same daughter whom he stays with now, in fact. He had joined the Prince at the start, & follow'd him in all his battles. On Culloden Muir he took a wound in the shoulder (he can shew you the scar of it). He crept to a dike and lay under it untill long after the fighting was over. They found him, but by luck the one who got him was an honorable man & did not kill him there and then. Any way, he was put on board that same Vessell that took Malcolm & his father & all the others to England. And after lying all Summer upon the river he was broght to trial, & sentenced to be banished over the sea. So he was chained together with a few others and put on to a trading vessell bound for the Indies. They were in the middle of their voyage when a storm blew up from the West, which swept some of the sailors overboard. And when the rest saw that the vessell was likely to break apart, they released the prisoners to help bring down the sails. They were alltogether ten weeks upon the sea, for the storm had driven them far back into the East. Their food was almost gone, & for six days the prisoners ate nothing. Then at last they sighted the wooded mountains of the first of the Islands they were bound for. But before they coud reach their harbor they were that very day set upon by a Privateer that came at them out of one of the coves. Half

the men were killed by the sword, sailors & prisoners both, & Donald Peter Angus was taken captive
upon the pirates' ship. They meant to sell him into
slavery. But he & two others untied their knots one
night whiles the vessell lay at anchor, & so made
their escape to shore. He had no knowledge of
where he was, only that it was some where in the
Americas. Then, betwixt lying low, and walking,
& stealing to eat, and here & there working for his
meat, he found his way to a Harbor, and he bided
there untill a vessell came in that was bound for
Britain. He at once made him self known to the
captain, & signed on as a seaman, and so worked
his passage all the way to the town of Greenock.
And so after five years he came home to his parents   (1751)
and his wife & child. And when at last he walked
into the farm the first one he met was his daughter,
but he walked on past her, for of course he did not
know her.

He said later that it was not alone his daughter
he did not recognise. He hardly knew his farm, or
his neighbors, or his Country it self, so much was
changed in those five years since the going of our
Prince. He thoght he was returned into a different
world.

You see, the King in England made new Laws   1747
against the Chiefs and the people of the Highlands,
in order to destroy us once & for all. He took from
us our freedom to wear the plaid, & to carry our
weapons, & even to play our pipes, and he denied

our Chiefs their authority with their people. When we first heard of these things we laugh'd, because we thoght it was some one's jest. Then, later, when we realised that the news was true, we still laugh'd, because London is a long road from Glengarry's Morar, & we thoght that all his German puffing woud hardly make even a ripple on our Loch. But we were wrong.

This was the way it happened. For a time after our Prince left us the people of our country believed that he woud soon return, with a ffrench army at his back, perhaps on the very next ship. And so we tried to prepare for that time, as best we could, by gathering together whatever weapons we had left, & other supplies. We hid them here & there thorow Glengarry's country, both Morar & Knoidart. But only Rumor came; *he* did not come. And meantime there were spies out amoung our people, and by some means they must have got word of our hoarding, for the whole country was soon swarming with sodgers, & for a few years they hardly left us alone. They were still amoung us when Donald Peter Angus returned. And it was a part of their orders to seize any man who broke the King's new Laws. One or two men were seized, in fact, and thrown into the prison at Inverness or kept in the sodgers' Barracks. And we heard of one man, from beside Loch Garry in the East, who was caught a second time & sent away to America. All in all it was pretty hard to dodge them.

And so most of us put away our plaids & pipes.

Some wove new cloth and made themselves Trews;
some sewed stitches in their plaids betwixt the legs;
a few boght flaxen trews from travelling men; some
– but not many – took a chance and defied the King.
And so it was allso with our Pipes. Their sound
carries far – far enough to reach to the ears of our
enemies. Some times we wou'd hear them far away,
sounding clear & sweet over the hill or across the
loch, & then of a sudden the tune stopt short, & the
pipes were hidden away. Old Neil Michael up at
Kyles had no opinion whatever of Kings or sodgers, and most days that next Summer he woud be
up at dawn, standing with his pipes upon a rock,
& he woud play all the tunes that he had learned
from the chanter of Patrick Og McCrimmon at his
school in Sky. Patrick was thoght the finest of all
the players of the pipes, just as his father was thoght
the greatest of all the makers of tunes. And especially Neil Michael wou'd play 'I Gave a Kiss to the
King's Hand' and 'McDonell of Glengarry', just to
remind the sodgers whose Country it was. He said
it started the day right. And they never caught him.
But most men's fingers in those days got out of the
way of the chanter. And the young did not learn
from the old, for it takes constant practice, & that
could not be had. And so in time, the more our
shame, most of the pipes fell silent. And the ancient
school of the McCrimmons was finished allso, and
is now almost forgotten.

They had a Law allso that a man could go to the
camps and give in his Weapons, without harm or

punishment. A few men did this, but it was mainly rusty & useless swords they gave up. Most of us hid ours some where about the farms, & that is what I did. The powder horn that my father gave me before he died I kept, for I had watched him make it when I was a boy, softening it in boiling water to get the shape he wanted, & I kept it for his sake more than for use. I kept my Pistol too, in the wattle of the wall. I have it yet, and I keep it shining. It is a good one. Look, you can clearly see the maker's mark: here it says 'Alxr. Campbell', and this word is 'Doune', that is the town where he made it. The King need not lose his sleep over it, because I keep it only for memory.

And see this Knife here. I can remember when it was a claymore, the length of a man. It was my grandfather's. But after our people were defeated fighting for James when I was a boy, my father turn'd it into a one handed sword. Michaelina's man's brother took it into England with our Prince, & to Culloden Muir, & when I got it back I cut it down again & made three knives of it. One I gave away. One I took to carrying in my oxter, in the old fashion'd way – there the sodgers cou'd not see it, & there I thoght I might need it at that time of spies. But it was never used. And this is the third one, I kept it for my meat, & here it lies on my plate yet. It is about as war-like as my self.

As to my targe, go out side & climb up on the thatch. You will see it covering the smoke hole and keeping out the weather. At least, that is what it is supposed to do. But with the years passing it is nearly worn away, & that old otter skin that used to keep off sword & pike now barely keeps off rain drops.

VII

St Peter in Chains

We later found out that when fferguson's men were burning Hugh's house they took the chance to search in his desk, and they found & carried off some of his papers. One was a list of the priests in the Highlands, & it was a great capture for it helped our enemies to hunt them down, They hoped that if they could seize the priests they woud cut away the roots of the Church, & it would soon wither. And this list told them the very places to find them.

There were one or two they coud have crossed off the list at once if they only knew it, for they were dead. Mr Colin had died on Culloden field – he was a Campbell & a cousin of Argyll himself. Another from the East whose name I do not know died in the straw in the gaol at Inverness. And there was a third who was taken away in that vessell to London, & died in a prison ship upon the river there. There were others on that same vessell, & that same prison ship, who survived it & were afterwards broght to trial & banished over the sea, losing every thing they had. One was my friend Alan from the White Island. Another, they say, walked ashore in a foreign land, and was at once set upon by robbers, & found himself alone there without so much as his shoes. After a while he slipt back and made for his Station in the Western Islands, but still for a few years he spent his days moving from hill to hill & cave to cave there, just as his Prince had done before him.

I believe if you could have met these men, they woud have had some tales to tell you, of the close escapes they had, & the tricks & disguises they used. In some places they coud only hold the Mass by waiting on the Saturday untill they judged it was past midnight, and then gathering quickly & secretly, and so returning to their homes in the darkness. But as to the priests themselves, even without their black cloathes they had need to move from home to home if they were to stay free, & never more than a couple of days in the same house.

They speak of one down the coast who was staying a few days in the house of an old woman, one of Borrodale's cottagers. This day they saw sodgers coming up to the door. It was too late to think of hiding. So the woman stood in the door, & when the sodgers asked her had she seen a Priest, for they had heard that there was one hiding in that country, she bade them come away in, but there was only herself and her poor lunatic son living there. At her back sat the priest with his tongue hanging out & his eyes staring up at them, moaning & gargling. I need not tell you, they hastily gave their excuse & departed to the next house.

Some of these things we got from Mr William, for before the year of Culloden was past he appeared amoung us again. It seems he was about the only priest in all the Highlands who cou'd do his work openly & in safety. And this was because of a Letter he bore with him, which he had got from the Sherriff of Campbell of Argyll himself, of all people, which permitted him to travel freely in all the Campbell country. They did not believe he was a danger to them, or one who might rally the people to the Prince, and in this they were right, because Mr William may have been a battler himself but he was never a man for war. Some say he even took an oath of allegiance to the English King to get that letter. Anyway, he used to wave it in the nose of any sodgers he met, & with it he moved pretty well anywhere he wished, in or out of Campbell's country, & they let him go about his work in peace.

For a few years he was the only priest we saw in all the Continent, North or South of the loch, and perhaps in the Islands allso, and the poor man hardly ever stopped in one place long enough to swallow before he & his horse were on the road again. By now he spoke our language like one born to it, but with all his travelling he would come away with words & sayings that we never used or heard of in Glengarry's Morar. Then Mr Wet-Today woud laugh at us for our ignorance, & tell us that the pupil had left the masters far behind. I think he spent near as many days upon the water as on the land, & whensoever he was in need of a boat one was put ready for him. Our oldest son Ian Beg was one of those who many the time rowed him across to Knoidart, or even on the open sea to Eig.

1750   Ian was sixteen years old by this time, and for a good part of the year, when ever there were fish to be had, he stayed over at Ardintigh with his three cousins & helped them in their boat. He was the fourth oar. It was his hope to learn the ways of sea fishing from them, & then in time to buy a share of their boat. When ever he came home he wou'd tell us the news from up the loch, and from the Knoidart side, & give us word of any vessells of the enemy nosing round the coast.

Well, it was about the longest day of the year when he came in the door to tell me of a couple of boats that were in the loch beyond Tarbert. There were strangers in them, and overhearing them as he rowed past he had taken them to be English speakers. They were certainly not fishermen, nor spies either, for they were making no attempt to hide from sight. One of them had called across to their boat & tried to converse with them, but of course no-one could understand him. Ian asked me to return there with him so that they might make themselves known to us.

We made our way to the bay of Tarbert, and seeing no boat there we climbed the road upon Drumcullin. Now we coud see Ian's boat lying out in the Kiles, & close by it the other two. The one was big & black, with a square sail & a smaller sail at the front, and it had its anchor down. The other was a boat of four oars, tied to the back of the first one with a rope, so that it swung gently round it with the current. We climbed down the road into Kiles farm, and Ian's cousins came in and broght us out to them.

There were nine men altogether, betwixt the large boat & the small. Their Leader was the youngest amoung them, he seemed not much above twenty. He asked me up into the sailing boat and there he told me openly who they were and what was their business. They were from the Low Country right enough. His own name was William Roy, & he insisted he was not a sodger, alltho' I saw some in his company carrying guns. He had been sent by his masters to make pictures of Loch Nevish, & every other loch and coast, & every farm whether on the shore or inland, not alone in Glengarry's Country but from end to end of the Highlands.

'That will hardly be the work of a day', said I, at which he laughed & told me that he had been at work on it for three years allready, & he believed it might be three more before he woud be finished. Every Summer he made his pictures, and when the days grew shorter he returned to Edenburgh & fitted all that he had drawn together there. He shewed me some he had made. There was one beautifull one, such as I believe you might see in the house of a Chief – it shewed the head of the loch, & he had done it with dyes★ so well that you might almost watch for the waves on it to move. But the others were only what he called 'quick pictures', done with the pen, shewing a farm or perhaps a bay as

This is the word Ian used, having no knowledge of paints.

you would see it from on the loch. And others I only understood when he had explained them to me – they were pictures that an eagle might draw from the sky, with dots & marks that he called houses, & lines close together for the corn fields, & a waving line where there was a river. These last kind had words writ upon them. I think he must have seen in my eye that I did not think a great deal of them, because he said that they were in fact the most important ones, & that when his whole work was finished he woud have one single great Picture of this kind made – a 'Map' was the name he gave to it. It woud be all of one piece, such as to barely fit upon the greatest table in London, & it woud have marked upon it every farm, river & field in the Highlands.

He told me that where ever he went upon this work he tried to find a man who could speak in his language, and tell him the names of the places of that country, so that he might write them in upon the pictures. He said that if I was willing to be his guide in this country he woud pay me for my serv- ice. I talked with Ian about his offer. He seemed to us an honest man, there appeared to be no harm or mischief in his mind, nor was he seeking the name of any man, whether gentleman or tenant. At this time of the year our women were away up at the Shielding, and I myself was idle, betwixt the cut- ting of the peats & the bringing of them home. So I said that I wou'd go out with him for three days on Loch Nevish, & if he wished it I wou'd do the same on our own loch also. But I wou'd not take his money. Instead he shoud draw a picture like the one he had done with the color'd dyes, & give it to me as payment, & a second one if we went on Loch Morar. And to this with a laugh he agreed. So for pretty well a week I lived with them upon the water, and at the end of it he had his names & I had my pictures. I kept them. I never gave them away, alltho' a few men have had their eye on them. I have them here in the house yet, & I got them out ready for you coming. They are a little faded – the colors were brighter on the day he made them. And this one is torn on the edge – it was one of Mary's children who did it.

(After we had looked at them & he saw how I admired them he continued:)

You may keep them if you like. I have no use for them now, & you must have occasion to meet many people who woud be interested to see them. I wou'd be glad if you woud wish to take them. And if, as you say, you are going to make my Memories into a book, then these can be the pictures for it!

The first day I went out with William Roy we rowed up the loch past Ardnamurach, headed for the farm of ffiniscaig. His sailors were working against the current, and as they pull'd upon their oars they sang to give rythm to their strokes, just the way we do, but in the English tongue. Some of their songs were of love, & some were in praise of the King. But the King they sang of was George.

And once as they were straining to drive the vessell forward, past us below our bows came Ian and his cousins seeking the early herring, & singing of our own King, & of our Prince, to the stroke of their oars —

> *Oh let us journey o'er water & wave*
> *Oh let us go over to Charlach!*
> *Ne'er to sit timid within doors at home,*
> *Oh let us sail gladly to Charlach!*

And I sang back down to them verses that my friend Alexander the poet had made and taught to me —

> *And should you come again to my Country*
> *Only Death coud drive us apart, my love!*
> *I woud follow you to the end of the earth*
> *If you, my love should come to ask me.*

William Roy enquired of me the meaning of my words in English, and when I told him he took them to be a love song. And so I suppose they were, for at that time every man of us in Glengarry's country, whenever we were upon salt water, still kept one eye open in case our Prince woud return. Like a girl scanning the sea, watching & hoping, and our heart skipping a beat & jumping up to our throat if ever we heard rumor he might be coming.

1752 It was two Summers after this that Bishop Hugh

slipt back into Glengarry's Morar. He stayed two days & nights in our house, with Mr William, and this was the chance for us to learn from his own mouth all that had befallen him since he had escaped from Mewboll. He told us that three years had past before he had been able to return from ffrance. After that he had at first lived in hiding in Edinburgh, & then when he took courage to go secretly into the Highlands he had still kept away from his own Country, & had settled instead in the East where his face was hardly known. From there he kept in touch with his people as best he could, & if a chance offered he wou'd venture out to visit them.

'But once I am on the road', he told us, 'I never stay long in the one place, and I am never the same man twice in any place. Today, if a stranger asks, you may say you have a visit from your cousin Hugh McAlister; but tomorrow it will be Hugh Sandison on his travells; when I reach Moydart I shall perhaps have become Hugh McKay. And if these shoes ever again return to Edinburgh it is likely Mr Scott will be wearing them. For none of these men walks abroad for long, & so I keep our enemies in the dark.★

'These are the things that we must do for safety. Even Mr William here, alltho' he has more freedom than the rest of us, we never use his own name if ever we have occasion to write of him in a letter. We call him "Hatmaker", for we never set down any name on paper that might be used against us

A note of explanation may be required here, for a matter that would have been clear enough to Ian. The Bishop styled himself 'McAlister' because his father was named Alexander, or 'Alister' in the Erse language, 'Mac' of course signifying 'Son'. Similarly 'Sandison' because he was Sandy's son, 'Sandy' being the familiar form of Alexander. By 'McKay' he intended 'McA', viz. the son of Alexander. Concerning 'Mr Scott', I can only surmise that he may originally have been given that name by friends in ffrance, as being the Scotsman in their company.

by a lawyer. We use secret words allso, for the same purpose. Let me shew you how it is done: wait whiles I think a moment ... Now, if you captured a letter and read this – "The Merchant in Oldtown must send money for our Shop, for training Laborers enough for all our Customers; the bearer of this letter you may know as Constantine" – what woud you learn?' He looked at us laughing,

'Nothing that is anything!' said I.

'Well, it would mean – "The Cardinal in Rome must send money for our School, for training Priests enough for all the faithfull; and the man who bears this letter is One you can trust". It is simple, when you know.'

'Your letters must make good reading', said Peggy.

'And they give us some diversion in the writing', said Hatmaker. 'And sometimes, if there is something delicat to be said, our Bishop will write a part of his in Latin, or I might write a line or two of mine in Italian, and so, one way or another, we keep the dogs at bay!'

Mr William was in great spirits that evening. No-one woud have guessed that he was often afraid & lonely, and that more than once he was near to giving up. But I know that it was so, because he told me one night when we had taken a drink together.

'It is not the labor', he said. 'I can happily endure that. But I have an aching longing for a home of my own, so that some times I hate the very road I have to travell on. Not that I have ever once been unwelcome in any man's house. But it is never my own house. When I arrive the people never speak to me untill they have knelt & received the Blessing. They expect me allways to keep myself a little apart – and that is a lonely thing to be.

'And then the country I have to travel is so great, & the people are so many, that I could never begin to give each one enough. The thoght keeps coming back to me that I am failing them, & their touching gratitude for every little thing only makes it worse.

'And when I see the freedom the Ministers have, and their houses & walled gardens, there have been times when I have asked myself whether God wills our ffaith to prosper, for we seem ever to be fighting a losing battle, and losing our best men, & watching for enemies over our shoulder. It is hard to live every hour of your life in fear.

'Do you remember when I confided in you once before? I thoght I had put those old regrets away long since, but the life I have had to lead since the defeat of our Prince has shaken again the walls that I had built. Many times lately I have wanted to get away from here. Sometimes, even, in my worst moments I have envied those priests who died at Culloden or in prison, & blamed God that this was not His will for me; despised my own obscure & unheroick task; even resented the sick I have to visit.'

Then he stopped short.

'These things I shoud not be telling you', he said. And the next day he charged me not to tell any man what he had spoken of, so long as he lived, and I never did. I am only telling you now to shew you the burden he had to carry in those days when our Church was in chains. And you know, when be revealed to me those weaknesses that he daily kept hid, I was deeply shocked at first, but afterwards I thoght not the less but the more of him.

Our oldest child Mary was twenty years old now, & there was no word yet of her marrying. In those days most girls were married by her age, or two or three years before it. But she was content upon the farm, and never so happy as when she was out with the cattle. Well, a couple of years past, & still no man in sight for Mary.

1754   As we all sat about the fire on the dark nights Peggy wou'd be praising this or that young bachelor of Morar, & one especially more often than the others wou'd creep into her conversation. But he was not the one that Mary broght to the house the week after All Saints' Day. It was a young man Calum Ian she broght, a dark haired lad from Bracora farm, well made enough but as shy as a corncrake. I need not tell you whether or not Peggy made him welcome. Any way, the other one was

1755   never mentioned again after that. The two of them courted thorow the Winter, and after Easter Mary asked to bring him home to speak to me.

'And do not keep the poor man waiting all day, the way my father kept you waiting, before you bring the Whiskey out', Peggy warned. She made sure nothing woud go wrong that day.

That Summer he was building their house beside his own people at Bracora, so that they might be married as soon as the peats were in. It was Mary's hope that Bishop Hugh woud return into our Country to marry her, since it was he who had baptised her. But he was in Edinburgh. In fact, all-tho' we did not know it, he was on the day of her wedding lying in the prison there, for some-one had betrayed him to his enemies & led them to the house he was staying in. And altho' they after-wards let him out because of his sickness – for the poor man had nearly died two years before – they banished him to the Border of Scotland, & there was no way he could get back into the Highlands. Nor was Mr William to be had, for he was away in Clanranald's country. So Calum Ian rowed across to Knoidart & got Mr Alexander, the young priest there, to come over to marry them.

Since ever the sodgers had ruined the Chapel on the White Island we had taken to using the Mass Stone at Bracora again, & it was there that they were to be married.

The night before the wedding the sun set golden clear in the West and the air was still, & Peggy was saying that the day might be as kind as it had been for our own wedding. But I saw the hills looking clearer & closer than they really are, & I feared that rain would come on the morrow. When we awoke the weather was changed, right enough, but still dry & bright, & Peggy said that so long as it stayed that way we could do without the heat. Before mid morning we all set out walking West. When we got up on the hill we cou'd see out beyond the Continent to the Island of Eig, with clouds hanging upon the Sgur of it. Peggy glanced at me, for cloud on the Sgur in the morning is a pretty sure sign that the sky is not for clearing. We were climbing down to Inver Beg when we first felt the wind from the West, & by the time we were on the path above Bracarina it was strong in our faces, & with a smir of rain in it. Now the cloud was coming down upon the hills around us, and we gather'd close about Mary as we walked on, keeping her in the midst of us. And so we got to Bracora, & the Mass Stone there.

The crowd was gathering. Mr Alexander was there allready, and four servers with him. They had a kind of Roof, made of an entire cow's hide, which they were holding up with poles, one at each corner, ready to keep the Blessed Sacrament safe & dry. By now the wind was sweeping over the hill, & the rain was flying straight, & we knelt on the West side of the Mass stone to put it at our backs. Then for a space it ceased, & Mr Alexander made a start. But when he reached the part when Mary & Calum Ian were to step forward it blew up stronger than before. He was shouting the words, the servers were struggling with their poles, and the cow's hide was writhing & tugging this way & that. At the very moment when he asked Mary, 'Will you take this man Calum?' – away went the roof and

three of the poles before she coud give her reply, &
we were a good while chasing it over the hill and
bringing it back and then putting it together, so
that he coud continue. For years afterwards, when
Mary had six of a family, we used often to tease
her and ask her if she was sure she was a married
woman at all.

The wedding meal had been set out in Calum
Ian's home down below in the farm town, because
our own was too far away, The moment the 'Ite
Missa Est' was out of the priest's mouth the whole
crowd of us ran down the hill, wringing out our
cloathes as best we coud as we went. And when we
sat down to eat you wou'd hardly have seen us for
the steam rising & filling the house.

Mr Alexander stayed for the first Health & then
he blessed the couple and away out into the rain he
went, headed for Knoidart. It was days like this that
broght home to us the hardships that the priests
endured for our sakes. And not alone the hardships,
but the Dangers allso. For when soever they were
upon the road their sacred things must go with
them, and any one might stop them & discover
what they were carrying. Earlier that same year a
priest had been captured in Glengarry's country
in this manner, & taken off to Edinburgh to the
prison there, & he had come out a dying man for
the cruelties he had suffer'd.

We talked of these things as we ate the wedding
meal, & it was around that table that we first began
to talk of having a church again in North Morar.

'It could have a house or hutt beside it', said Peggy, 'where the priest might keep his possessions safe, & take his rest.'

'Or he could even live there', said Ian Beg, 'if the day shoud ever come when we have a priest of our own again.'

'And it wou'd be no harm to ourselves either to have a roof above us', added Calum Ian's father. 'It was the Mass stone that was the death of old Catherine from your own farm last year, and of Donald Bracarina allso, & it may be the death of more yet after today. We have had a few buried this past year or two following weddings on the hill.'

We spoke of our idea again when we next saw Mr William, and he agreed with it. So we began to make plans, & look for the best place to build. We chose the spot of flat ground beside the burn at Inver Beg where the road runs close to the shingle strand, because it coud be easily reached by land or water. Boats coud be left safely there, whatever the quarter of the wind, betwixt the little Headland on the West side & the great one on the East. And no-one betwixt the farms of Beoraid and Tarbert could quarrel with the place, because it is about in the middle of them.

We wanted it to be a church of stone, not like a house to be pulled down after a few years. There were at this time just one or two houses in all of Glengarry's Country that were made with stone, & a couple of men who had some knowledge of building in this manner. We knew allso the size that we wanted – fifteen good paces from end to end, & four across inside, with walls to the level of a man's eye. So we coud judge what stones we woud need, and the length of the roof tree, and the number of roof beams. We even began to gather & prepare some of these things. But we knew that we coud never begin building whiles the Country was full of sodgers.

Well, our chance came the very next year, because that Autumn they were all marched away to fight in the War against the ffrench, & that was the last we saw of them. The Harvest was in, and our plans were made allready, so we were able to make a start almost on the day they left. There were men from every farm went to lend a hand, so that we might have as much as possible done before the Winter, & I was one of them. **1756**

I recall the first day I went. Mary had given birth to her first child a month before, a fine strong healthy boy, & she had broght him over to Brinacory. Peggy had him outside to get the fresh air on him, & she was bathing him in the big half barrell that she used for the milk. As I started up the road I turned and looked back at her sitting in the white sunshine at the end of the house. She was singing down to him, with her grey head leaning forward over the barrell, and her sleeves rolled up & her feet tucked back. And I saw again the brown haired girl I had first set eyes on, the day I met her at the milking.

We built the Church to face the East, with a door

at the back, & one on the South side looking out upon the loch, and an other on the North side facing towards the road. We set the altar stone a litle in front of these doors, with a wattle fence of willows behind it to make a room at the Eastern end. It was only later that we built a solid wall of stones there. Nor at first did we build the priest's hutt onto the side, the way you have it now. We were hurrying to have the church fit to use as soon as possible, and it was a few years later before we added on the hutt. What we had at first was a short wall sticking out by the side door, so that the priest might put on his vestments there once the people were all within. He wou'd stand beside the wall to do it, on one side or the other of it depending on the way the wind was blowing. And before he came in he wou'd make his horse's rope fast to the wall, & leave him to graze there.

We had the walls up soon after All Saints' Day, but after that there was never a clear week of weather untill March for us to carry on the work. So on Christmas night we were still under the stars, like 1757 the shepherds of Bethlehem. By March we had a roof on, but only above the Altar, and when we gathered on Easter Sunday morning, coming from every side & each of us carrying his own turf to kneel on, it was still under the sky we knelt. We put up the last of the roof in May. Now we were out of the wind & rain, and we coud leave our turfs just inside the door and lift them as we came in, before we took our places, the men on the left &

the women on the right.

You know all these things as well as I, for they are still the same today. But when we first built the Church there was still the fear of spies in the Country, & that is why we put no windows in it – it was more against the eyes of enemies than for the cold that we built it that way. May be if we were to build it today, now that we are free, we woud put windows in it. And yet, I believe we wou'd all still wish it to be the way it is in any case, lit with the glow of fir splinters on Winter days, & with sunlight in the Summer when the doors are thrown open.

The day it was finish'd we got word across to Bishop Hugh. It was welcome news for the man who had lost his own house, & his chapel, & a good few of his priests. He was in need of good news at this time. For when the War had started against the ffrench some of the gentlemen of our Country & Knoidart, and of his own & the Clanranalds, had left to become officers in the English King's army. In those days any man who did this must foreswear his own Catholick faith & accept the Protestants' religion, and these men had been willing to do it. Colla of Barisdale's son Archie had done it. Kinloch Morar had done it. Worst of all, two of Hugh's own brother's sons had done it. They did it to get back their land. But I can tell you, when they sold their Honor to buy the favor of enemies they lost the trust & friendship of their kin. And when the War ended & they returned home from the English

King's army, they came as strangers into their own Country. Many of us never really trusted them again. For, as the old saying is, a man does not roll about with the pigs and come away clean.

As for Hugh, it was one wound more for a man who had allready taken many.

VIII

Fishing with Ian Beg

By this time Ian had become a partner with his cousins, & the four of them were prospering, for there had been three years, one after the other, when the Herring came in good numbers into Loch Nevish. Then, just a few months after we had the Chapel built, their boat was caught in the first Autumn storm, beside Gewish Island where there is nothing but clifts & rocks, and as they went in to seek shelter it was overturned by the tide rushing out of the narrow channel. Ian caught hold of a ledge and pull'd himself up on to it, but his cousins could not reach it. All three were drowned, and only one – that was Donald – was ever found, cast up upon the shore the next day in the bay at his own farm at Stouil. It was his mother her self who found him. They buried him close by the high tide there, as is the way when a man is taken by the sea.

The boat itself they got all right, beached upon the strand over at Inverie, & it was hardly damaged. Ian went across for it, and because he knew that it is ill fortune for a man to keep a boat after it has broght death in to his family, he arranged to exchange it over in Knoidart. He found three brothers in the farm of Glassgile who were happy to take

it for their own boat, for theirs was older and less
well made. So Ian came home with a worse boat,
but with a boat at least. If he had had to buy one
like it new at that time it woud have cost 75 Mks at
least. For nets it would have cost nearly twice that,
but those he had no need to buy either, for his own
six good Irish nets he had saved from the sea, all in
one piece and the buoys with them, allthow a few
needed the bladders made water tight & nearly all
lacked mouth pieces & stoppers. The main net rope
was the kind made of plaited fir roots, that will neither sink, nor rot, nor break, and it had held every
thing together.

Ian decided that he must tan the nets anew, if they
were to last, & that Winter he & Peggy & I did the
job. And some job it was, because you must steep
each net, a portion at a time, in water boiled with
oak bark, & then do it all a second time. But when
it was finally done he had a boat fitted out that was
nearly as good as the one they had lost. Now all he
lacked were men to be his partners.

1758   And so it was that at the age of fifty three I began
a new life upon the water, alltho it was against my
best judgment that I agreed to go with him. I was
born & raised a man of the inland loch, not a man
of the sea like the farmers of Loch Nevish side,
whose first sight in life is the salt water. I had no
love or trust of the sea – how wou'd I have, or Ian
either? So it was for the one Summer only, untill he
could find partners, that I said I wou'd go.

It was the custom then, just as it is yet, for all the

fisher men of North Morar to gather together in the bay at Tarbert before the Summer fishing began, for the Blessing of the boats. We knew when the herring woud be coming. It is allways about three weeks after May day, as soon as the wind turns in to the West, for that drives them in from the islands & they follow their King in to the lochs. We were watching for the gannetts gathering & diving in the sound betwixt Sleat and our own country, & we knew that we should soon after catch sight of the first rippling upon the surface of our loch that woud be the sign that our visitors were arriving. Then all the boats were broght round in to the bay. One of the vessells belonging to the farm at Tarbert was anchor'd & fitted with planks of timber, & every other boat was tied up close about it. The priest climbed upon it and from there blessed the sea, & the crews, and every boat – stay, sail, mast, rope & anchor – sprinkling the nets of each, and then he himself untied the first one and let it go.

And so we rowed out thorow the Kiles and in to the upper loch, whiles the herring were held in there by the tide. We had our nets roped to the buoys, deep enough but not too deep, & if by chance the shoal was found swimming too near the surface we had stones ready, to drive them deeper down where we wanted them. We coud see at once that it was going to be an other good year – may be the best yet, said Ian – and before the dawn we were back at Tarbert with a boat full. We got what we cou'd into baskets, but more than half we had

to throw away. We broght what was left back home
before they woud be wasted in the heat of the day,
& the women smoked them upon a fire and hung
them up under the roof.

Ian was not mistaken – it was the best year ever
for the herring, and the only year whilst I was on
the sea that the Busses came in to Loch Nevish.
Untill now the Buss men had allways done their
fishing on the far side of Knoidart, where the greatest numbers of fish are to be had, but as soon as
they got word that the biggest shoal this year was
in our loch, they were not long in coming. And
this we thought was good news for us. It is true
that they were forbidden by Law to buy fish from
us, and could take away only what ever they caught
themselves. But we knew that some times a Skipper
woud allow us to sell to him, one way or an other.

That first evening we lay out in the loch &
watched them coming in. We counted eighteen
of them, and none with less than ten of a crew.
Each one had a rowing boat behind, and the larg-
est had two or three. Once they had their anchors
down they wasted no time. Whiles the sky was
still golden out in the West above the jagged hills
of Sky they sent out their row boats to lay the nets.
The biggest of them had maybe thirty nets roped
together in a line. All thorow the night the rowers
worked their way along them – we coud see them
in their pools of light – emptying them one after
an other and bringing their loads back to the men

upon the Busses. Again and again they did it, untill the Sun had gone round under the earth, and was coming up again in the East and glowing allready behind the black shadowy mountains at the head of the loch.

We knew better than try to sell to them after their night's labour, but waited untill the afternoon when they woud have slept & eaten, and had drink taken. Then we looked for the biggest of them, & I climbed abord her expecting to speak in English, for we guessed that she woud most likely have come up from Greenock. But as it turned out she was from Campbelltown harbour, & all her sailors had the Highland tongue. There were fifteen men on bord in all, above or below her deck, & she was carrying close to a hundred casques in her hold for storing fish, and over a hundred barrells of salt. The Skipper told me that he had no need of my fish, for there were enough in the loch to fill his ship twenty times over &, as he express'd it, they were fighting one an other to be first in the nets. But he said it woud be no harm to him to take as many fish from me as woud fill half a casque, & he was willing to give me 5*l*. for them.

'I will sell them for 18*l*.', said he, 'but after I have paid for the barrells & hoops, & for mending the tackle, & paid off my men, I will be lucky to see 2 or 3*l*. clear for them'.

I offered them to him instead for 2*l*. & enough salt to fill a barrell a sixth way up, and he agreed. It suited him to save the money. As for us, it was the salt we needed most, to keep our own fish fresh for eating.

The Buss men made their camp upon the shore at Kiles, & each day it grew bigger. They broght their empty casques & their salt barrells on to the flat land betwixt the river and the fields, as close to the corn as they dared, & they laid out their curing yards there. Each Buss had its own salting trough, with the casques lying on their sides close by, ready to pack the fish. It was here that our salt was measured out for us, & we linger'd there to watch them at the packing. They did it with layers of herring & salt alternate. We saw some casques that they kept apart, which they intended to sell to merchants from the Indies, & in these they put twice the measure of salt because the men of those Countries prefer to eat their fish strong pickled.

Along the shore they put up huts for sleeping in, which they made with branches cut from the trees of the farm. And close by, soon after, tents of woven cloth & skins appeared, like mushrooms in the night, set up by people of our own Country come there in the hope of getting work. Some whole families had come – the women and young children to clean the fish, & the men and older boys to help with the nets and the salting, or to sell cattle meat or drink to the sailors – and they stay'd as long as there was work to be had. But we ourselves tarried no longer than to get our salt, and then we headed home. As we climb'd the hill, with never a stir in the air or on the sea, I remember looking back at the camp with the smoke of a dozen fires rising dead straight into the evening sky, and across the Kiles on the Knoidart side an other camp & other fires with their smoke rising straight.

It was only later that we heard of the trouble between the men of our Country and the Buss men. It happened when the men of Kiles found their own nets entangled in the great nets of the Busses. They had allready seen their timber cut down & broken, & the edges of their fields trampled flat. Their meadow was poisoned with salt close to the curing yards, so that no beast woud go there. Then, near the end of the week, some of the Buss men got drunk, & one was seen to make lewd advances to the older girls when ever they past by his hutt. At once the men of Kiles gather'd on the edge of the Buss men's camp. It is certain that someone's head would have been broken that day, but that both sides held back (as we supposed) because they knew that if ever Blood is spilt upon a shore the herring at once leave that water. And they still had some fish to catch, so they held off. But in the morning the Buss men found many of their nets cut away, & some of the buoys bursted or set adrift in the night whiles they were waiting for the tide.

For a few years after that the greatest shoals of herring found other lochs to visit, and the Busses did not return. Most of the people of our Country were glad enough, except those who had found work with them. We were well rid of them. The only thing we missed was the chance to get salt from them, for that meant that we had to throw away what ever fish we could not cure at once. There was no other way of getting Salt at a price we cou'd afford, even suppose we had been willing to travell the length of Scotland for it. But the fishermen of Ireland were permitted to buy their rock salt cheaply, & the coal to burn it. And we learned that there were men amoung them who were willing to sell it secretly at a price we might afford and still at a profit to themselves. And so it was that some fisher men from our Country took to sailing out beyond the islands to the North coast of Ireland, & bringing a boatfull of salt back to sell amoung their neighbours. Some of them did it every year. They woud wait untill the Spring gales were past, but it was a perilous business whenever they did it. Two men of Moidart were drowned trying it; & any way to be caught at it was to face the Hangman.

There was a man John Joseph from Mallegvore – he is dead now, so you can put his name in your book. He was of an age with Ian, & he used to make the run every year, so that he got the name of 'The Salt Man'. It is his children Donald, John & James that you will know, and that is how they are still always known as 'The Sons of the Salt Man'. He used to bring other things back in the bottom of his boat also, as I have good cause to remember.

1761 We had gone two years with no Busses to get salt from, and we not knowing when next we woud see them (if ever), so we made up our minds that before the next Summer came in we woud take the boat round to Mallegvore whenever John Joseph was returned from Ireland. Well, we met up with him and got our salt easily enough, and it was coming from his house that I bump'd into my old friend Alexander, & that was the beginning of our troubles. He had allready a good drink in him and he was for getting across to Inverie, for he had lived there previously for a few years and he had taken a notion to visit his friends there again. He proposed that we get liquor from The Salt Man and take him & ourselves across in comfort, When we saw the barrell of rum he had in mind, we easily agreed. John Joseph drew us enough rum to fill a milking bucket, & it was agreed that we wou'd pay for it and the salt when ever we sold fish to the Busses, if they should come that year, or else when we next sold cattle to the drovers.

'God bless the Barge of Glengarry!' says Alexander as he stept in and took his perch upon the very prow. 'Follow your helmsman, boys – sturdy, keen eyed, watchfull, ever calm in the face of the storm!'

First we swallowed a couple of mouthfulls. Not a drop was going to be lost out of that bucket, for it was a dead calm day, & the flattest sea you ever saw. Another swig and we pushed off. Alexander at once fell back into the bottom of the boat, and there he lay with his arm over the side, pointing into the North, and muttering now and then –

We will go forward with every danger
As long as we have four boards left . . .
Or even a couple of spars still nailed together ...
As long as she is still floating under our feet
Or one single peg remains above the water!'

Before we reached Inverie the bucket was empty,
& we were full, and no more sea-worthy than the
Helmsman. I seem to remember that we gave the
boat a crack upon the rocks as we came in. We slept
in someone's house, and in the morning the woman
had sea pinks gathered & boiled, and a drink made
of them ready for us, and with its help we managed
to live with our heads. And we still had The Salt
Man to pay for the pleasure.

It was not only herring that we fished for. They
themselves are gone as Winter comes in, but many
other kinds follow them along the coasts & in to
the loch. In the New Year cod are to be had, &
we used to catch them and sell them if we coud.
And in the same nets we set for them we caught
other fish allso, haddock & eels & whiting most
often, and these we took home and kept for eating
in Lent.

The Seal was an other fish that was caught in
those days, for they were very plentifull then. So
many were killed, in fact, that you will see few of
them now in Loch Nevish. Any one was permitted
to take them from the water, but once they came up
on to the rocks by the shore, where they are most

easily caught, then they belonged only to the farm whose shore it was. I have often seen men catch them on the rocks – the best time was the heat of the Summer when they came up with their young. The men beat them to death with stout wands, but many escaped because it took quite a few blows to kill them, even if they were able to strike them correctly, full upon the head. I have even seen the adult seal return after she had escaped, & face more blows trying to push her pup before her to the water, & often the mother and pup together were killed that way. The seal's flesh is mainly kept for the children and old people, & it is the very best meat for sickness of the stomack. The liver allso can be used as a remedy, and the beast's whole body is full of oil that burns well & gives off a good light.

The fisher man saves his best tale to the last, as they say, so let me tell you about the one we caught out in the sea that next Summer. It was one morning in the midst of a week of fine weather, & we were on the Knoidart side, with two men of Kiles in the boat along with us, rowing West betwixt the bay of Sandaig and Skerryglass. Ian had told me of the Kerban fish that now and again comes down betwixt Sky and the Continent, & even in to the loch, but I myself had never set eyes on one. Usually, if you see one at all, he has his mate with him. But this time, when Ian shouted and caught my arm, it was just one on his own. He was lying to the West of us. He was much longer than this house & byre. We

1763

could see the whole back of him, & in the midst of his back a fin like a ship's fore-sail, and beyond that again part of his tail. He seemed to be lying asleep on the water, but as we came closer upon him we could see that he was moving forwards very slowly, with his mouth wide open, and drinking in the sea. It seemed to me that he might easily get his teeth round the front of our boat, if he wished, but Ian had no fear of him. He wou'd have left him, even so, for the very size of him, but there were two other boats close by, out from Sandaig, & Ian said he believed that between us we might capture him. The others must have had the same thoght, for each boat was moving quietly forward.

He saw us all right, but he was not inclined either to swim away or to attack us. We were so close now that we coud see the great gills at the back of his head, & the water coming out of them in waves. Ian took up a spear, and pass'd the other one across to me, whispering to me to aim as close as possible to those gills, whiles the other two held the boat steady. I cou'd see in the tail of my eye the Sandaig men doing the same. Then we all threw, at allmost the very same moment, & three or four of the spears stuck fast in him. In an instant he dived under, as deep as he was able, & we cou'd see his shadow in the green water twisting and trying to shake out the spears.

And now he was off and racing away beneath the surface, out to sea, untill he reached the end of our ropes. Then our three boats were drawn along, and we were digging in our heels and pulling back, like men trying to halt a run-away Horse. If the sea had been anything but flat calm we woud surely have capsized. He took us this way and that, and all the time we were trying to steer him in towards the shallow water. For an hour we fought him. He took us out beyond Romasag, and then in again, running along close by the shore, & I mind the sun was out over Eig before at last we cornered him by the farm town of Airor. Then we drove him close in, & surrounded him, so that he stuck upon the sand and was unable to turn or move. We leapt into the water and attacked him with the rest of our spears, & had him dead in a few minutes. The people of the farm were out, cheering us on. And so we tow'd him back in to Sandaig, in the mouth of the night, and in the morning we cut him up and shared the meat. His liver we kept apart, & at the end we cut into it & got from it oil enough to fill five barrells. Some of my own share I kept for the house lamp, but most of it I gave to our families in Brinacory & Swordland for treating the hides whenever they were making Brogs.

I told you that I first undertook the fishing with hesitation, & never thoght to stay beyond the one Summer at it. Yet I believe that in the end the salt air I breathed found its way into my heart, and a love of the sea grew within me as if I had been born to it. The creak of our oars became my Music. And sometimes even now when I can do litle more than sit, a sea longing comes on me, and a restlessness to make the run to Knoidart, maybe, or step again upon the Island Across. When storms strike this roof I am put in mind of black nights when Ian and I struggled with the wind & the current in the Kiles. Or on a warm Summer day, if the hills of Morar are sharp and clear, I mind the day on the blue sea amoung the islands as we rowed close beside a strand, & we could see far in the West (if you will believe it) the white smoke of the kelp burners rising above Uist.

1764   But as it turned out, the year after the War ended was my last upon the sea. And my last journey of all was to Inverie. We stayed a few days there. The farm, along with all the others on the lands of Scotus and Barisdale, had been seized for the English King after the defeat of our Prince, & in those days it had not yet been given back. The King's ffactor had broght in masons and had an half dozen new houses built there, made in the Lowland way with stone & lime, & he had given them to foreigners who had been in the King's army in the war. He thoght he wou'd make farmers and fishermen of them, but we heard later that all but one of them let their land go to ruine & afterwards slipt back into the Low Country with the Bounty the King had given them. A school master had been put there allso, with his own stone house and school room, and the best of land with a share of shell sand & tangle for his corn. It was the Protestant Church that set him up there, to try to make the children change their ffaith. They paid him a wage of many Ls every year, with an other payment of the same from the King. This was to teach their Catechism, as well as reading, writing & cyphering, and all done mostly in the English tongue. While we were there some of them came from the North to visit the master, to satisfy themselves that he was teaching the things they wanted, and it seems they went away well pleased. They talk'd of bringing a Minister there allso, and building a house for him on good farm land, but if so nothing ever came of it.

Betwixt them, and the master, and the ffactor, they were full of plans to change the people of Knoidart & make them live like Low Country men. They had a rule made that the farmers must allways sow pease after oats, alternate, and an other rule that permitted no man to keep goats, either on his fields or even on the hill. They even broght a man in to catch the foxes & rats & eagles, and gave him a house and money every year for it. Some of these things you could see the point of, or their plan behind them. But for the most part, no one knew under the white sun why they did them.

We were five days at Inverie when ffergus came over in a boat from Tarbert looking for us. He broght news that Peggy had been taken suddenly ill, and was lying in her bed hardly able to stir or breathe. We got word at once to Mr William – for at that time he was the priest for all of Knoidart as well as Morar – and by God's good care he was that day staying on the Knoidart side close by at Killichoan farm. The stone bridge had been that very Summer finished over the river there, so he got to us with no difficulty. We raced the tide to Tarbert, and once on land the four of us ran the length of the road to Brinacory, & thank God we did. As we went in at the door all our family were crowded in there allready. Ian looked at me. We both knew without hesitation that Peggy was close to her death. She was sleeping, and only once did she stir & open her eyes.

Mr William prayed with her for a few minutes and blessed her. Then she beg'd us all to look after one another, & she held her children, and I kissed her for the last time in this world. The rest went out a while, and I sat beside her alone, talking to her a little without answer, and thinking to sit thorow the night with her. But I must have dozed, for when I awoke she was allready dead, and her hand still in mine.

I remained with her a while then, sitting in the clothes that she herself had woven & fulled for me to go on the sea in. I thoght of her at the fulling, and leading the singing of it. All my kindest memories of her were at the singing, for she seem'd to me to have sung her way thorow her life. And I thoght of all the days I had been away from her, and she praying every day we were in the boat. I wished then that I had spent them with her, and never again since then have I gone out upon the sea.

The next day our house was allways full, and at sunset we gathered round her bed for her Waking. Three times we prayed the Rosary for her, & then the old ones made songs around the ring in praise of her. Someone took up the pipes, and I made a start to the dance. And so we waked her untill the sun came round and up again.

Mr William came then to say her Requiem, & after it ffergus and Ian and I bore her out & buried her next to litle Michael's grave. It was a black December day, and the hail started up and flew full in our faces as we prayed, young & old, kneeling amoung the grass, and then it stopped as suddenly, leaving the land and all our coats covered in white.

The Summer after her death, I was sitting in the house when in at the door came Catherine – she was the fourth of our children who lived.

1765

'There is a man come from afar to visit you', she said, 'and his name is Hugh McAlister. And he wishes me to tell you that he has three friends with him, a Mr Sandison, a Mr McKay ...'

'I know', I said, 'and one by name of Scott.'

'A blessing, Ian', said Bishop Hugh, embracing me, 'and God's blessing upon Peggy, may He be mercifull to her. I am across in the West for a week or two, as I try to be every Summer, & I have called upon you for old friendship's sake.'

'Do you know, Hugh', said I, 'it is more than half a hundred years since first we became friends.'

'And what wisdom have we to shew for them all

but grey hair?' said Hugh.

That first year crept by. There have been nearly thirty more like it since, & each one as long as the last. And now that I am old, old, I am all the time waiting — just as she used to wait when I was away upon the sea — and I have no desire for an other year on this earth.

IX

Lost harvests

It was four years after Peggy died that our young Chief Duncan came of age. And now that he was able to do as he pleased with what was his own, he wasted no time in shewing us the kind of man he was. Allmost at once he sold our country of North Morar, & all the farms within it, to McHimmy's son, the Chief of the Clan ffraser. He paid his debts by selling his people. It was a thing we had not ever dream'd could happen. It was a thing that his forebears woud have died before they did it. But of late the Chiefs of Glengarry had shewn that they were no longer the loving fathers of their people. And so, alltho' we were amazed at the deed that he had done, yet perhaps we had reason to hope for better times from it.

But at first, for sure, it did not seem that better days were coming. For hardly had the land past into the hands of Lovat than three years of lost harvests fell upon it, and they were years that broght us grief upon sorrow.

I remember well the first Spring. We had had a week of warm days, & the whole land was awake, and we were even thinking of an early sowing. Then the wind turned. For a day the sky was clear & the air raw. And then we saw the deer coming back down off the hills, & we knew that the snow woud follow them, and so it did. It lay two weeks, & behind it came a month of rain and sleet. So the corn was late into the ground, & late to grow. Before it was nearly ripe the Summer was away and the Autumn coming in, wet with never a break. One or two men cut it while it was still green, having nothing else to feed on. And when at last we got a couple of dry days together our priest gave permission for us to work on thorow the Sunday whiles we had a last chance. Even then, most of us lost half of it. And so there was less to eat, & less to keep for sowing.

Since potatos had come to North Morar – and that must have been close to twenty years before this time – we had allmost forgotten the days of drinking the blood of our cattle, but that next Spring I know of families who took to doing it again. The rest of us had eaten nearly all our grain, & kept back only the least we dared for sowing. We sorely needed a good Summer to give us a high yield, but we got no kind of Summer at all. So the Harvest was thin, & again it was slow coming. This second year more men broght it in still green, even some who the year before had scorned their neighbors for doing it.

Some became fishermen who had never fished the sea before. But with nothing wherewith to buy salt, & litle salt to be had in any case, the fish must either be eaten at once, unless they coud be smoked, or else thrown away. There were families eating

1770

fish that were already rotten, for want of any other food. A child died at Bracara on All Souls' Day, & people said that this was the reason. A cousin on Peggy's side from Romasag managed to find buyers for fish he had caught – where I do not know, for there was no money in the land. Any way, with whatever he got for them he made the journey over the mountains to the town of Bewley & came back with bread. He told us that in the country he past across, which was far from the sea, the Hunger was even greater than here. On the journey back he was obliged to hide the loaves under his coat & pretend to be looking for food himself, for fear of his life.

Before we got to Christmas I made up my mind that I woud try for salmon in our loch, as others were allready doing, alltho' I had despised it all my life and its flesh had never untill that time enter'd my belly. I got out the Spear my father had made, that I had kept stuck under the roof ever since I married, never moving it except when I built a new house. You can see it still sticking out up there, just above the wattle fence.

(He asked me to fetch it down. Then shewing it to me he continued:)

My father searched a few days before he found a willow branch that would do it. And see how neatly he weighted it at the sharpen'd end with stones bound on to it. This is the same original rope he twisted for it out of goat's hair – I had no need to twist a new one when I took it down, for it was as good as new after half a hundred years, and it still is today. The dampness can not rot goat's hair, you see.

On the good days of Advent you'd find me down to the East of Brinacory Island, for that was thoght the best place, with half a dozen others, all standing up to our waists & each with a spear resting on his shoulder. But for all the hours I spent there I believe I caught very litle except aching bones.

Night was the better time, if you had a boat & a lanthorn, for the salmon is curious to follow a fire, & so he overcomes his shyness and approaches close enough to be taken with a spear. Quite a few men kept their children alive that Winter in this way. I mind one night standing just up there on the knoll & looking out over the loch. It was a night of blackness without star or moon, and I coud barely see the path I trod on. But out in the blackness I saw the fires of the fishermen, & alltho' I coud see neither land nor loch I coud judge exactly where they were. There were three over by Letir Morar, & a couple by the Mewboll river, & four or five more out off Swordland, and one far, far away up the loch. All in the world I coud see were those tiny fires, as if they were floating in a great dark pit. And as I stood there – if you will believe it, and I a grandfather – I began to think that they might be the souls of those who had died of hunger, come out into the night, watching & winking. And the longer I stood there old sleeping fears awoke in me, so that soon I was hurrying away from the sight, as fast as I coud feel the road beneath me.

The Gentlemen of the farms cancelled many of the rents in North Morar that next Spring, by the agreement of McHimmey's son, since the people had neither money nor food to pay with. It was then that we were glad that he had boght the Country, because no such kindness was shewn by Glengarry in Knoidart. But it was at this time, also, when the second lost harvest was shrunk to the last few grains at the bottom of our barrells, that men began to talk of leaving the land, if there was only some way they could get to the Low Country.

But there was worse coming. That year the first frost came earlier than I think I ever remember it, & it was frost that covered the trees & lasted thorow the day. We cut our corn with red hands, but the frost had wasted it before ever we had it in. Some were still cutting it in December. Whatever litle we got that coud be used, we knew woud last us only to the New Year and no more − & then a Spring and a Summer lay ahead of us without any hope of food. Two or three men, ones who had had no harvest at all, gathered their families & what ever they possessed, there & then, & sett off over the hills in the hope of finding food in the Low Country. Cottagers with no land began to move hither & thither, without a plan. The oldest just lay in their homes.

By now my daughter Mary and Calum Ian had six of a family down at Bracora. The oldest of the girls was Anna. She was a bonny lass of ten, & tall for her years, and I believe she was my favorite because she had Peggy's brown hair and her eyes. For a year or two at this time she used to spend most of her days with me at Brinacory looking after the house for me, for she liked to do it & it left one less for Mary to feed. Well, this morning soon after the New Year she woke me. We had had a good fall of snow in the night, & she shewed it to me & begged me to take her out in it there and then. So out we went, with not a sound in all the world, and not a footprint of man in the snow, & we began to tread where we guess'd the road to Swordland lay. As we went up over the knoll there, I was watching the Loch and the wisps of smoke rising from it. But Anna was stepping ahead trying to find the road, and she called out to me, 'Does it run beside that Hump there?'

'There is no mound by the path just here, nor a rock either', I answered, 'unless the snow has broght one down.' But we could see nowhere that so large a stone might have rolled from. And we saw now that it was not one mound, but two close together.

'It might be early lambs', said she as we pushed closer thorow the snow that here lay drifted deep, & she lifted her skirts & skipt ahead of me. And then she turned. Her eyes were round. She said nothing, but struggled across to me, and then tugged me foreward. Even before we reached the place I knew what was there, for I had caught sight of a child's knee sticking out from the whiteness. We brushed some of the snow away. It was two litle boys we found there. They lay close together and the smaller one was gripping his brother's coat. I looked at Anna. Her young eyes were filling with tears, and she came in under my coat. I led her quickly away from the place, telling her that we must hurry to send for the priest. Before we descended over the hill I looked back at them where they lay like poor dead birds in the snow.

Later that morning someone found their mother, a good few steps further back upon the road, lying in a heathery hollow under a rock. We guessed that she had been overcome with cold & hunger, and that she knew there was a farm town over the hill, & she had sent her children on in the Blizzard to try to find it.

That snow did not lie many days, and after it came rain without cease allmost untill Easter, with winds that broght a plague of sickness upon our cattle. Every second beast in our farm died of it. We heard the same story from Swordland and all the farms, & at Beoraid there was not a single animal – milch cow, stirk nor heifer – but perished. I believe it was the same in Knoidart, & beyond the mountains allso. So now we had nothing. No corn. No cattle either to eat or sell. No means to buy a loaf, even supposing anyone had the strength to journey to find one.

Near to the end of Lent the storms died away and the skies cleared, & the day before Palm Sunday we woke to a frost & sunshine on the hills. My son ffergus said that he was for taking a walk over

to Swordland to see was all well with his mother's
people there. But when he got there, before going
down into the farm town itself he climbed up
into the hill to the old shielding where his cousin
Michael stayed. (That was Peggy's sister's oldest son.
He had been given a strip of land there when he
married, & he had his house built upon it.)

As ffergus climbed into sight of the house he was
expecting the two daughters to run out to meet
him. But neither they nor Michael were to be seen.
As he came up closer he caught a snatch of a lullaby
'. . . holy Angels bring you slumber, Blessings many,
without number', coming from within. He pulled
open the door and stood upon the entrance. Marion was sitting by the dead fire, rocking her baby
in her arms. She did not notice him, even when he
spoke. At first he could not see into the corners of
the house at all, coming out of the sunshine. But
as his eyes became accustom'd to the darkness he
looked about. There was nothing, neither food nor
furniture. The bench & the chair must have been
used for the fire. Upon the bed of heathers lay what
he took to be cloathes piled, untill he looked more
closely. It was the two girls & Michael, lying each
a litle apart, & their faces had been covered with
a blankett. Marion was singing still, in a whisper,
& now & again she woud break off as if she had
forgotten the words. It was the dying singing to
the dying. He watched the sleeping child, and the
mother's song turning to steam in the air, & there
came to his mind words from a different lullaby,

A sleep that no morning will break,
A frost that no Spring will make green.

He ran straight back to Brinacory, and called in
here and gave me the news. And then he set off
again at once for Inver Beg. He knew he wou'd
find Mr Aeneas there, for it was his custom to go
there every Saturday & stay in the hutt over night
to be ready for the morning. As soon as ffergus was
away I myself set out East with Anna, taking whatever milk & oats we had.

As we approached the house all was silent. I made
Anna wait outside, whiles I went in. I can remember every detail of what my eyes saw, but I woud
rather say no more about it.

After a while Mr Aeneas came running over the
hill, with ffergus at his heels. He came inside and
prayed for the dead. Then we lifted Marion and
the baby off the floor, & laid them next to the others, untill we coud bury them. Anna was in there
beside us now, and she was sobbing as if her heart
woud break. I held her head against my breast.

'See how peacefull they are', I whisper'd, 'and
tonight they will be sleeping on Christ's arm.'

'There are some in North Morar who will be
envying them', said Mr Aeneas to me.

The house was left unused after that, & the good
land around it no-one woud dig. Over the years
the roof has begun to fall in. You can see a few
houses up & down our Country that have lain the
same from that Spring, without song or laughter

in them – the saying is true enough, that going to Ruine is silent work.

Thank God for our bishop & our priest at that time. John was our bishop now – Hugh's sister's son. He had been made a bishop a dozen years before, and by now he was in charge because Hugh himself was too old & sick for travelling. John lived on the farm at Buorblach and two Summers before he had repaired the big house there with his own hands to be a Seminary for boys, just as Guidale had once been for himself, and the White Island for Hugh before that. Once it was ready he had broght Mr Aeneas in to live there with him and be the master. Aeneas was young & strong, and I heard he was very good with the Scholars, but he had to give the lessons as best he cou'd with hardly a book for their use. John made him the priest for North Morar allso, whiles he himself spent most of his days travelling, trying to help wherever there was greatest need, from Moydart to Knoidart and from Loch Garry to the Islands in the sea. He had to be bishop & three or four priests together, because his own priests were too old to look after their people, or even, hardly, to look after them selves.

Our own Mr William was only hanging onto life by this time. He had been staying down at Keppoch since the year after we buried Peggy, and he had sunk fast after leaving us. He was younger than me, you know, a good five years younger, but he had never been a strong man. Now he could hardly leave his house. He was nearly blind, & his legs & arms were full of pain & stiffness. They say it was pitifull to watch him say the Mass, for every few minutes he woud stop, & lean upon a wall or chair to get back his strength. At last his old stomack sickness was grown so bad that he was not able to get beyond his door.

He stayed alone, and I believe had any one stayed with him they would not have found him easy to live with. He had allways been a fiery man, even in good health, & now no-one had a great wish to go too near him in his sickness. So as soon as the New Year was in Mr Aeneas was sent to tend him, and he woud sit with him in the day, & sleep at night in a house close by. The women of Keppoch took turns to leave in food for the two of them, & to clean the house. Anyway, this night Mr Aeneas had left about an hour before and one of the women called in to smother the fire, & she found Mr William down on his hands & knees, catching his breath, & crying out in agony. She turned and ran up the road and shouted for Mr Aeneas, & he threw on his coat and ran back ahead of her. But he arrived too late. And so for all their care Mr William died in his pain alone.

As a mark of respect Morar himself took on all the arranging of his funeral. We buried him at Kilmory, and many from North Morar, like myself, made the journey over the Muir to be there. Three dozen years he had been in our country, and many from young to old had good reason to love him.

1773

More than one in that long time he had seen into this World, and then out of it. And even at the last his thoghts were for his people, for he had instructed that upon his death his books & furniture shoud be sold and the money be given to the poor of our Country, & God knows there were enough of them that year. His own inheritance he had order'd to be shared amoung the priests & amoung the poor people of the East where he was born & raised. He was a good man and a good priest. He had been my help & consolation when Peggy died, & alltho' we had not seen each other since that time I counted him a friend. May God be mercifull to him and reward him.

The truth is, the people of my generation were going one by one now. And with the Hunger on the land it was not alone the old who were dying. That year there seemed to be death upon death, barely a week passing without a funeral, & hardly a single baptism. It was as if the whole country was broght to its knees.

My old friend Bishop Hugh we never saw now, for he stayed over the mountains in Glen Garry and never stir'd from there. They say he was like an old horse that had been worked to the point of death, & since the Autumn he had not risen from his bed. The Winter, & the deaths amoung his people, had broght him so low that he barely had the will to eat. He coud not hold his pen, nor his book. It was old Mr Aeneas who told us these things, for since the death of Mr William he had been staying beside

Hugh & tending to his needs. But as it turned out
he did not tend to him for much above a month.
It was Lent, with the days growing longer, and
this evening he stayed on into the night with him.
They were talking together, & Hugh even seemed
brighter than usual. And then, allmost in the midst
of what he was saying, he rested his head down
upon the pillow and closed his eyes as if overcome
with a sudden wearyness. When Mr Aeneas bent
over him he cou'd see that he was dead.

May God be mercifull to him and reward him.
His death left Bishop John allmost alone, & I never
saw a man grow old so fast as he did that year. The
only fit helper he had was young Mr Aeneas, & it
must have been a sore choice he made that Summer
to send him beyond the hills amoung the people of
Glen Garry, because that left the boys in the School
without a Master. He himself was spending most of
his days away and was rarely at Buorblach to look
after them.

First he broght in his nephew Mr James to be
the new Master, & he kept him there for two or
three years. Then he broght in Mr Austin, who
was an Islandman, & that allowed Mr James to be
our priest.

The farm & the house at Buorblach were held in
tack, but ever since John had got hold of it he had
been trying to buy it, with all the ground to the
North as far as Glasnacardoch, so that he should
have a school that wou'd endure, & not be for ever
moved from place to place. And now he thoght that

this was really going to happen at last, for McHimmy's son himself had made a promise to sell the land to him.

1779 And then without any warning, we got the news that he was dead. The feaver had taken a hold in Knoidart that Spring, and many of the Morar fishermen had ceased calling in there, for fear of bringing it back into our Country. Bishop John had gone over at once to be with the sick, and he made visits to every farm from Brumasaig to Carnoch. On the eve of May day he was at the Kiles, bringing the Blessed Sacrament to a man they thoght was dying there, & it seems it was from him he caught the feaver. The man himself recover'd & is living yet, but John never moved out of that place, and in five days he was dead. They broght him to the enclosed ground at Killichoan farm to be buried, and for all the feaver there were many came from outside Knoidart to pray him into the earth.

Once we had lost our bishop we soon lost the school as well. I believe you must have heard how it happened – how Mr Alexander (that is Sandaig's brother) had hoped to be chosen to take John's place as our Bishop, but was past over when the choice was made; and how it was Sandaig who soon after that persuaded McHimmey's son to break his promise & sell the farm to himself. I do not need to say more. Anyway, the farm was lost, & the school 1782 had to be closed, & Mr Austin left our country. Mr James stayed on with us for a few more years, untill you your self took his place.

So now I have broght my tale right up to the time that you arrived in this Country, & the rest untill the present day you will know better than I.

(He sat back, & took out a pinch of snuff, & set it upon the knuckle of his thumb.)

'But you must finish the story you began, having come so far with it', I said.

'All right!' said he with a laugh, 'I am willing to do it. But not tonight!'

X

Leaving the land

Do you remember the summer that you came 1782
here? Our corn & potatoes were both mostly
lost that year, and it was a long Lent of fasting we
had in the Spring that followed it. And that Spring 1783
itself do you remember? It was not what could be
called a Spring at all. It was as if the Winter waited
on to make acquaintance with the Summer. And
then that, when it came, was short & wet, and ended
early with the Autumn frost. And so again we lost
most of what we had planted. We were beginning
to remember the Hunger of ten years before.

To make it worse, there were so many to be fed.
Since ever I was born I never recall such a number
living in our farm as there were at that time. As our
children had grown up & married they had been
given shares of the land, some in the fields down
here and some again with new fields up at the
Shieldings. And it was the same story in every farm.
There were so many of us now that we seemed to
be living with our feet in one another's mouths.
We all got by, so long as the harvest held good. But
if ever the Summer failed us, as it did those two
years, then we were hungry again.

And if we cou'd not pay our rent with corn or
potatoes, how cou'd we pay it at all? Selling our

cattle hardly broght us enough to cover it. Those who lived along the coast cou'd maybe pay part of it with kelp, or with whatever they got from the fishing. But not us. And yet, allthough we each now had less land, every year we were called to give a greater rent for it, so that – good year or bad – the daily care hung over us to find the means to pay.

Since I was a young man there had been men from our own country here who left the land, & headed for America to make a new home there. Some had gone there to escape, after our Prince's army was scatter'd. And later there were others, as I told you, who joined the English King's army in the war against the ffrench, & at the end of it they were given land in America as a reward. Word used to come back from them from time to time. Then after that, when McHimmy's son led the Highland men to fight against the American rebels there were some from here who went with him, since they were no longer forced to take an Oath against their ffaith. That war ended the year after you came to be our priest, the very year of our worst hunger. Some of his men came home, & told us stories of the Country there, and the farm land that was to be had. Others remained there, but they were no longer safe in the territories held by the Rebels, so they made the journey into the North & were given new land there which had belong'd to the Indian savages. 'Upper Canada' it was called, and the word they sent back was of a Country where you wou'd get more land than you could ever plant, & you could call it your own, & owe rent to no man; where fish without number could be taken from the loch, and fowls from out of the tree.

Well, when this came back to the ears of poor & hungry men it sent a tide of Discontentment rising up over our Country. Not the old ones like myself, but the strong young men, & the mothers carrying infants at the breast, looked about them at their own thin riggs. And the thoght came into the heads of some of them that, now the sea was safe again from the enemy's ships, it might be possible for them allso to make the journey to that Promised Land.

Then the year after that, over in Knoidart, Glen- 1784
garry got back his old land of Barisdale, and no sooner had be got it than he raised all the rents and began to lay out Sheep Walks there. It was in his mind to drive a good part of his people out alltogether, & they knew it. Some of them went to their priest – that was Scotus's son Alexander, you must have known him. Just what happened then I do not know, but I believe he must have talked about it with Sandaig, who was one of the Gentlemen who were returned from America after the war. Any- 1785
way, during the next year they found betwixt the two of them a hundred families in Knoidart who agreed to try the voyage to Canada, & pay for their share of it, if a vessell could be had to do it. So as soon as the Winter snow was melted Sandaig and 1786
Mr Alexander made ready to journey to the town

of Greenock to get a ship there. And when news of this went round, more men of Knoidart, and some allso from our own country, gave their word that they too woud make the voyage. In the end more than five hundred agreed to go, if you count the women & children.

All of Knoidart, so they say, was like an ants' nest with the coming & the going, the getting ready and the rumor. Word was coming back that they had got a good, sound Vessell of three masts, with a captain who knew well the Western Sea, & we were to keep our eye open for her any time after May day.

By now my grand daughter Anna was a woman of five & twenty, and she had grown into the very image of Peggy the way she was the day I first saw her. She was married three years to a Knoidart man, & they had a first son. Ian Ban they called the litle fellow, for his hair was as yellow as the primrose. One day that May she came to visit me, with the boy holding tightly to the corner of her shawl. I mind the shawl well, it was woven the colour of heather flowers, and as to Ian Ban, it was the first time I had seen him on two feet.

She was just the same girl who used to stay with me, & I believe she allways will be. She was hardly in the door but she set about preparing a meal for us, & then she ran thorow the house sweeping it and making it tidy. Ian sat upon my knee meantime, whiles I cut him a whistle from a sicamore twig & shewed him the way of blowing it.

'I have made an other poem for you, Dada', she said as she sat down beside us (for there is poetry in her family, you know, on both sides). I said to let me hear it, and she recited it to me, quietly & shyly. Some of the words of it only I remember –

> *We will take our leave of Morar,*
> *Arasaig, and Moydart of the high hills,*
> *Eig, and white Cannay of the surf,*
> *And beautifull, fair Uist.*

I told her I thoght it good, & that I supposed it was telling of the ones who were to sail with Sandaig.

'It is', said she, with her eyes lowered, 'and it is telling of Ronald & myself & Ian Ban.'

Then she told me of their plans, and how they had saved the 60 Mks for each of them that was the price of their place in the ship. And with shining eyes she told me of their hopes. And when she departed, promising that they wou'd visit me again before they sailed, & I watched her walking out in the sunny May morning with Ian asleep in her shawl, I understood well why they were leaving, & I saw that they were wise to be doing it. Yet I knew that her going wou'd be as good as her Death to me, and that howsoever long God might spare me in life I wou'd never again set eyes upon her in this world.

It was Mid Summer day in the afternoon when the

great black vessell put her nose round the point at
Mallegveck, and before the sun went down she was
lying at anchor in Inverie bay. There were three
masts on her, right enough. As soon as they saw
her coming the people began to gather from every
side, and to make their farewells, for they thoght
she woud be sailing on the morrow. But in fact
they were a week getting her loaded. I know you
did not get across yourself, but our Bishop Alexander was there, with Mr Alexander Morè from Keppoch, hearing Confessions every day, & on the last,
which was a Saturday, he gave Confirmation to all
those who were of age.

That night a good breeze blew up, and upon the
morrow Sandaig told the people that they were to
sail that afternoon. Everyone who was to make
the voyage, and those of their families who could
get there, and pretty well all the rest of Knoidart,
gathered on the strand at Inverie, & there at low
tide Bishop Alexander said the Sunday Mass, along
with Mr Alexander More, and Mr Alexander Scotus who was to sail with his people. We speak of
it yet as 'The Mass of the Three Alisters'. In the
crowd were Anna's brothers Donald & Patrick, and
her sisters, and her father Calum Ian, & her mother
Mary my daughter. They say there must have been
close to two thousand there. A table was set up,
facing the hills, and the people were kneeling upon
the strand below it, so many that the knees of the
last ones were allmost in the sea. There was a Mr
John there allso at the back of the crowd. He is the

master of the Protestant school at Inverie, and they say he is a good man. He was there to bid farewell to his pupils. He was standing beside Calum Ian as he knelt at the water's edge waiting for the Mass to begin.

'You know', said Mr John, 'I was thinking, we could all be banish'd over sea for this, even myself, if there was any way that such a number cou'd be rounded up & captured. Just think – the whole people of Knoidart banish'd out of their own land by an English King.'

'The King has no need', said Calum Ian, 'whiles Glengarry will do it for him.'

Afterwards, when the Bishop had given the *Ite Missa Est*, Mr Alexander Scotus spoke to the crowd.

'This good wind that blows our hair is the one that will take us to the New World, please God. Now let every man, woman & child who is to make the voyage take a stone from the strand, & we will make a Cairn of them just here at the mark of the high tide, at the place where our Country ends and the Ocean begins. And put a pebble in for the infants, if they are too young.'

Before the cairn was finished the tide was allready beginning to rise towards it. By now the small boats were hastening to and fro to the ship, carrying out the passengers. Three hours they were at it, untill everyone was abord. Then those in the ship & those upon the shore were waiting, and waiting, and now & then someone woud shout something across.

And then suddenly she was moving. A cheer went up from the vessell, and last words were shouted from the water's edge. Then as she moved away the crowd began to run along the strand, and where it ended they climbed up and ran beside the fields. The oldest soon gave it up, but the rest kept running round along the coast, a few dropping out here & there along the way, untill the fitter ones reached the strand by the Red Skerries, & they stopped there and watched her pass behind Skerryglass. Then off again they ran, cutting in over the land behind Rua Roanall and out to the furthest point. Donald & Patrick were amoung them. There they stood and watched her untill she past the Point of Sleat and slipt behind the clifts of Eig. Four or five fishing boats were at her heels, & they followed her thorow the sound betwixt Eig and the Island of the Forest, and there they let her go, and watched her sailing in to the South West, with the hills of Barra far away on her right side, untill she was no more than a full stop on a page. And then the sun dropt down from under the clouds and appeared above the Western horizon, & threw a brilliant glitter upon the sea, and amoung it they finally lost all sight of her.

About the time of St Brigid's feast a letter arrived back in Knoidart from Mr Alexander, telling of their safe landing. He wrote how that first evening on the sea they had watched the hills of their Countrey slip away, and as darkness fell they were allready abreast of the Western islands, & they could see one or two lights on them. But in the morning there was no sign of them.

That day they made a mark upon the side of the hold, and they did the same each day after, counting forty & three with no sight of land before or behind. Most of the days they were blessed with blue skies and following winds, and at such times the hatch was thrown open and they were permitted to walk upon the deck, but only a portion of the families at one time. Then allso the women cooked their food in the open, in boxes filled with sand so that the fires coud easily be put out. Even at night the hatch was often left open, long after everyone was settled below upon the pine boards, & before they fell asleep they wou'd lie a while and look up at the square of sky above them full of stars. Rarely were the sailors forced to close down the hatch, so that the air below remained clean and fresh. The bucketts were emptied morning and evening, and alltogether not one of all the passengers was taken gravely ill during the whole voyage. Only one day and a night, he wrote, when they were kept below deck in a heavy sea, & most of the children and many of the men and women too were vomiting, they lay trying to find comfort and thinking that the motion of the ship woud never end, & that night there were some who woud not have cared if she had gone down.

On the forty fourth day they sighted land, & everyone believed that they wou'd be stepping upon it

on the morrow. But what they took to be the Continent was only great islands. And even after they
had past beyond these they were then only entering
the firth of a River, but one so wide that they could
only see one bank of it. In all it was seventeen more
days and nearly a thousand more miles they had
to journey, from the day they first saw land, untill
they put down anchor at the town of Quebec.

There they walked ashore, but still their journey was far from over. Now they had to follow
the course of the river, and it took them an other
week for only the women and the younger children
cou'd be carried in the barges that had been provided. The men and the older boys kept pace with
them on the path beside the shore, and where that
left the bank and cut thorow the forest, as it did
in many places, they lost sight of one another. At
nights they slept under the trees. So they reached
Montreal Island, and there they were told to wait.

Close to a month they waited, with the cold of
Autumn coming on, untill new barges were broght
in that bore them on up the river. After three more
days they turned inland, and entered the Country
of Canada, and came at last to a town called Charlottenburg, where they were to receive land and
make their homes. There on the very first night
Mr Alexander wrote his letter, & sent it back with
the skipper of the barges with instructions that it be
carried down to Quebec & put upon a ship there.

He has written more letters since, and from them

we have learn'd how they are faring in their new homes, & who have been born and who have died. Every family, as well as each unmarried man, were given their own farm in the first week after they arrived. But a farm in that Countrey is not like our farms, where one man's rigs are set amoung his neighbours' and change from year to year. There all the land remains their own, and is measured in the shape of a great Rectangle★ with boundaries that run exactly straight whatever the hill or river that might stand in the way.

Ian's word was 'long square'

Some of the farms they found had allready been settled by men who had fought in the wars, and these were divided tidily into fields. But their own farms were just mainly forest without end, & their hearts sank at the sight of them. Those who had no settled farms next to their own might have to walk two miles to see their nearest neighbour, thorow the woods along paths made wide enough for only one man, with never a sight of the day, & with marks that they call 'Blazes' cut in the trees to guide them.

The children were terrified of the gloomy place, untill they grew accustomed to it. And at first many a grown man bitterly regretted coming there and wonder'd how ever he would feed his family, and many a mother allso as she tried to keep her children warm. For the snow began to fall allmost as soon as they got there, and before long it lay deep to the waist. Berries were their food, that first Winter, and tents of branches their shelter, for they had no chance to prepare any thing better.

But they saw the houses allready built by the settlers and in the Spring they began to build their
own in the same manner. They felled the nearest
& straightest trees, cutting them into loggs, & with
these they made their walls and doors, sealing the
cracks up with moss and clay mixed. With young,
thin trunks they made their roofs and covered
them with tree bark fixed down with pegs. Only
the fireplace and chimney they built out of stones,
setting it into the wall of the chief room to make
the whole house warm. That first Spring every
man made sure to plant a rig or two of potatos, &
to have his house finished and his wood stack piled
high by Autumn. Searching for the timber was
no hard task – there was enough on every farm to
build a hundred houses & a thousand wood stacks.

Whatever trees they felled they then dug out by
the roots. Others they set alight & burned, untill
they had enough ground clear for planting with
corn in the second Spring. And once it was clear,
& mixed with the ashes of the trees that had lain
thorow the Winter, they found it gave as good a
yield as the best land in our own Country. And so
the second Winter went by a great deal easier than
the first, and each year after it a litle easier again.

Mr Alexander wrote us that now & again they
saw families of Indian savages upon the river, or
down at the office in Charlottenburg. He had been
told stories about them by the settlers, of how they
worshipped a God in the rocks, & one in the river,

& an other in the forest. But he had never stood close beside one. And then one day early in the first Spring he made a visit to the last settled farm on the far edge of the town, and when he departed from the house there he thoght he wou'd take a stroll further into the forest. Soon he came to a place where the ground had once been clear'd of the great trees, but now it lay over grown again with bushes. Finding it green & pleasant he sat down to say his Office there. But he was not long sitting when a shadow fell across his book. He looked up, & saw two Indian men standing before him. They were allmost naked, and they had birds' feathers tied to their wrists & their brogs. They were carrying bows, & he coud see bundles of arrows behind their shoulders. Before he coud think to move these men knelt down upon the grass at his feet, & touched his Book, and then they put aside their bows and each made the Sign of the Cross before his astonished eyes. They beckoned to him to walk, and he went with them to their camp, where the women gave him food & drink. There was a man there to whose tent they broght him, for this man had a litle of the ffrench language, & betwixt that and the language of signs Mr Alexander learned from him that years before, when the ffrench held that part of the Country, there was a Priest who had often visited their camp. He had taught them prayers and the Gospel, & had even baptised a number of the families. But they had seen no priest since then for forty years. Mr Alexander promised that he wou'd visit them as often as he could; and he kept his word. He saw them frequently after that, & because he was their friend they sometimes took courage to venture into the farm lands.

Whenever they appeared they taught our people many things about that Country. They shewed them how to hollow out a tree to make a boat, and how to know when they cou'd walk safely on ice. They taught the boys to rub the grease of the bear upon their bodies when they went to the river to swim in the Summer, to save them from the bite of a kind of fly they have there. They even took the women to a tree in the forest which gives a sweet drink at one time of the year and a kind of soap to wash with at another. They shewed the men the best parts of the rivers to trap the salmon (which they consider the best of meat), and where to make holes in the ice to get them when they are frozen over, for even the running rivers freeze in that place. They shewed them the hiding places of deer, and great oxen they call Caribew, & how the flesh of all these beasts can be saved for eating all Winter just by burying it in a mound of snow behind the house.

'We are all turning into Indians, right enough!' wrote Mr Alexander in one of his letters. 'And now that we have begun to learn the ways of living in this New World, we have to endure no hungry season of the year here, as you do in the Old. Reading all these things, you will be beginning to think that we have landed in Paradise here! But remember the bears that enter our farms & kill our cattle with a blow of their paw, and the trampling down of our corn by the Porcupine (that is a species of hedgehog of the stature of a dog), the mosquitos we must suffer in the Summer, and the shrivelling cold of Winter. And reflect allso that in Paradise, so we are taught, the soul will have no yearning, but here there is not one of us who does not daily feel in his heart a longing to look again upon Glengarry's Country and his people there. But then, when ever our spirits are broght low, we have a ready cure to hand – we bring out the Pipes from under the bed!'

Many times I have a picture in my mind of Anna doing the things that the letters speak of, & of Ronald clearing the forest and planting the land, a litle more every Spring, & of Ian Ban growing tall. And never a day goes past but they are in my prayers.

It was the second Winter after they left, on a grey morning of February without wind, that our son Ian Beg came in at my door.   1788

'I have news for you', said he. 'Our Prince is dead. I heard it last evening & I came over to tell you as soon as the weather woud allow me. May God be mercifull to him.'

We talked for a while, and each of us was thinking a hundred thoughts.

'I was eleven years old when he came to us', he said, 'and I was twelve when he went away. That is more than forty years ago, yet if he had returned today I woud have stood at his side with a sword in my right hand without hesitation.'

'I know you woud', I answered, 'and I too woud have done any thing that might be of use, though it woud not have been much. But the young ones know nothing of him except stories, and even some of the old hounds who remember him, and bark loud now & then, have long since come to love the fireside rather than the muir. For long enough we have known he was not coming.'

We walked out, & I pointed to the grey hills beyond Mewboll.

'That is where I had my last sight of him', I said, 'when he made his escape. It is as the song says –

> *The hills on which we watched you walk*
> *Have lost their brightness & their colour*
> *Now you will not return for ever.'*

'Michaelina and I were talking last night', said Ian, turning to me. 'We are thinking of saving & trying to get to America. Perhaps in a year or two, when our youngest coud go with us, and our oldest will be old enough to chuse. I think I have caught all the fish that this Country has to give.'

1790　　As it has turned out they have not gone, and I do not think they ever will go now, for Ian will be sixty years old next Spring, if I can believe it. But a good few others have gone. In the fourth Summer after Anna went an other Vessell sailed from down the coast at Lochnankeel. She was a much smaller ship though. Most of her passengers were from the Island of Eig, but about a dozen were people from here in North Morar. They were put ashore starving, and in the very mouth of the Winter.

The year after that an other ship went across from Clanranald's Country, and our Mr James went with them as their priest. Then two Summers ago I heard that more of Glengarry's people from East of the mountains sailed out from Garrison. And just this Summer past a few more of his people from Knoidart went on a ship with the men of Glenelg, but we hear that they were driven back by storms, and set out again in a new vessell only last month. The Blessed Virgin protect them, they will be sailing right into the Winter ice. 1791 1792 1793

Hundreds upon hundreds have left Glengarry's country this past twenty years, any that had enough money saved to go. Some have been so set on going at any cost that they borrowed the money they needed from Gentlemen on their ship, and repay'd their debt by working as their bond servants when they reached America. Some I believe have even sold their sons & daughters as bond servants to do it.

And you know better than I – for I am stuck here in Brinacory – that there are hundreds more who woud do it if they coud. America is where they have set their hearts upon. But if America they cannot pay for, they are willing to go to the Low Country or the East. Two brothers from our farm went only last year to the town of Stirling, for they knew it well from their Droving, and they have settled there and found work. Their plan is to save money untill they can get away across the sea. And my daughter Mary's youngest son, Donald, who is to be three & twenty next month, is dwelling in the town of Inverness. He is working in the Hemp Manufactory there, making sacks (he and sixty other men) from dawn untill dusk.

There are others who have gone to Glasgow. Whenever they get there they go straight to Mr Alexander More, who is the priest of the Highland men in that town now, & he takes them to where work may be had. Donald's brother Angus went there last year, as soon as the harvest was in, and Mr Alexander took him to a man who agreed to hire him to make barrells of timber. He came home this Summer for the cutting of the peats, & told us about his life there. He said that the houses are built high into the air, & lean over upon one another so that they allmost shut out the sky, and there are narrow paths in amoung them where thiefs lurk at night. He said that on Winter days whiles he builded his barrells beside an half dozen other men by the help of candles for the litle light that came in at the window, many the time he woud have given his week's payment just to hear an other man's voice speaking the Erse language.

'The Highland man was not made to labour for a Master, or live like an ant in an ant hill', said he. 'God meant him to have his own land to dig, & a Cas Chrom to dig it with, and a hill under the sky to herd his cattle on. I am not for going back to Glasgow.'

But this Autumn he went back, all the same, and a good few others with him.

For now that we are at War with the ffrench again, and it is not possible to get to America, more men than ever are heading for the Low Countrey. But as soon as the fighting is ended, they will begin to cross the sea again, nothing is surer. Why shou'd they stay? I woud go myself, I can tell you, if I were fifty years younger. Perhaps when the next ship sets sail, so long as I have not reached a hundred, I will be on it! For the news of the death of our Prince has broght the truth home, that the old world that I knew is gone for ever.

XI

The world I knew will soon be gone for ever

I visited Ian for the last time on the eve of Advent. He had in his company young Donald, his great grand-child. The litle boy's father was that same eldest son of his daughter Mary whom Peggy was bathing at the house end on the day Ian came to help build the church here at Inverbeg. Whiles Donald played beside us Ian talked to me about the world that the boy was growing up in.

In some ways, right enough, it is a better life now than the one I was born into.

There is Gold in the sea today. For a few years past the Buss men have been coming into the lochs in far greater number than before, because of the Bounty that is paid to them now. And our fisher-men are permitted to sell to them at last, so they catch as much as they are able, & none is wasted. All that they do not eat themselves is turned to Money – such as Ian Beg & I never thoght existed.

The Drovers are prospering allso. They can sell every beast they have and more, and at a high price, for all the beef that can be got is needed for the War against the ffrench. These days they drive them far into the Low Countrey, to the town of ffalkirk. That is the same town where John Grant had his home, & the tryste there is far greater – so the Drovers say – than the one that John and I sold our cattle in at Crief. Once they pass over our mountains at the head of our loch the whole road to ffalkirk is black with herds, like lines of moving ants. And once they reach Garison they have a gravell'd road to walk beside for the rest of the journey. I believe if William Roy were to make his Maps again there are a few new roads that he woud need to draw upon them.

But few are the corn fields the drovers pass beside these days. They see litle on the Highland hills now but the big sheep of the Low Country. For myself, I do not believe that the hills were made for herds of sheep to roam on. A sheep does not care for the Bent Grass that the cattle love, nor does his dung manure the ground. To me he was allways a woman's beast, & I do not believe that he will ever bring us good fortune. He has brought no luck to the people of Knoidart, for sure.

This War has also filled the purses of the men who burn the Kelp. Its value has doubled in the past three years. They can get maybe 50 Merks in a Summer for it today, and quite a few of the farmers of Loch Nevish-side are to be seen cutting the weed off the rocks, or gathering the tangle where soever it is thrown up onto the shore. Then they draw it along behind their boats in bundles to the places where they have their pitts for burning it. This last Summer or two, if the breaze has been in the North, I have sometimes caught the strong smell of their burning coming over the hill as I sat here in my door.

The War has taken many from our farms to fight in the King's army. No longer need a man foresweare his ffaith to become a sodger. It is said that the Catholick sodgers are even permitted to have their own priest to say the Mass for them. I suppose they need us now, so they are pleased enough to take us as we are. Anyway, more are sure to go, & some will not return.★ Yet who in my youth could have believed that these men wou'd be fighting for an English King, whose fathers' fathers fought beside our Prince *against* one? But then, that Prince forgot about us, long before he died.

('You know that only last year a new Law was made, which permitts not alone sodgers but all the Catholicks of Scotland to follow their religion openly at last, & us priests to travell freely without fear of spies', said I.)

We all heard about that Law. I never cared much about the Laws of the Low Country, or of Sherriffs, or of English kings, & I do not believe that any was ever made with good intention. So I will wait & see with this one, for it may yet be a Snare. But yet, when I sit and think of the forewarnings that Mr George gave to us boys on the White Island, & Bishop Hugh and those others in prison, and men like Mr William broght to their grave by work & care, then I must thank God that I have lived to see this new Law made, if it means that Donald and his kin will grow up in a freedom that we never knew.

This very year, after Alexr the young Chief of Glengarry came of age, he got permission from the Govt to form a new Regiment of the Army, to which was given the title The Glengarry ffencibles. His kinsmen who were allready in other Regiments were permitted to transfer into this new body, & others enlisted into it who were hitherto in none. A priest was allso given them, to be their Chaplain. Translator's note. 1794

Do you remember when the School Master Alexander made those verses for Peggy in praise of Morar? 'Land hospitable & blest by fortune' – that is what he called it. And so it was for us. And, please God, it will be so for you, Donald Beg. Yet who woud have believed that it woud ever be in the hands of a ffraser? Who could have foretold that Glengarry woud ever sell his Land & the people on it? It used to be said that all the salt water in the sea will not wash out our Kinship. But what is kinship now? No longer does the Chief decide the Law, & settle our quarrells; no longer does the vassall fight at his side. The one has forgot his love for his lord; the other seizes all the rent that he can. Litle is the Kinship betwixt them today.

When Peggy & I were to be married I worked a while for payment at the Mining and the Droving, as I told you, but outside of that we saw little of money in those days. We knew litle use for it. We paid our rent in corn and service, & what soever we needed we made for ourselves. But now it seems many a new husband must buy even the clothes & the shoes he stands in, because many a young wife has never learn'd to spin, nor to weave & dye her cloth. Some of them woud not know where to find a blue or a yellow on the hill. They still know the words of the fulling songs, all right, but how many know how to full the cloth? King George took away our freedom to wear the plaid, but now that we have the freedom given back to us, who remembers how to weave the cloth for it? And he made a Law against our weapons, so we hid them; but we threw them away at last, not because of him, but because we had neither Chief nor Prince to fight for.

Whose hand holds the sword today? Whose fingers weave the withies of a currach? Whose pluck the strings of the harp, or tune the drones of the pipe? Rarely does the Great house today give Honor to the piper, or Hospitality to the bard, and poetry is as silent there as the lips of my friend Alexander, who has lain twenty years in the earth above Loch nan Keall.

Who wou'd have believed when I was young that so many woud leave the land? When I went away myself, & others like me, it was allways to return again. We never had thoghts of any other home, nor dream'd of any other world than this. But now it seems that the hearts & the eyes of the young are ever somewhere else.

We never dream'd of any other world than ours, & we had no thoght that it wou'd ever change. But the old, certain things of my youth – they are gone, as surely as the old striped Arasaid that my mother wore is gone. I see Change all about me, & the world that I knew is melting away like smoke in the wind.

Last week Ian Beg's wife Michaelina came to visit me. She has the gift of the Two Sights, as her mother and her mother's father had before her, and at my entreaty she consented to tell an old man something of what she has seen. She said that the day is coming when the people of our Country will travell West in order to go East, & when the words we understand will be dumb in their mouths, & when fish will leap South over the Morar river in their thousands. I do not know what she meant by these things. But she allso told me – and this was easier to understand, but harder to endure – that Brinacory will stand empty; that sheep will rub their flanks against the altar of Inverbeg; that our people will be scatter'd & an other race will take their place here. And the goodness of the well will not be known untill it has dried up.

('If this is true', said I, 'then like the seeds of the dandelion they will blow away and take root somewhere else, whether in the Old World or the New. And the things they have thoght good, & worth holding onto, will go with them and take root there'.)

You may see some of this happen, then, but not I. I am as old as a Hebridean. There are few betwixt the mountains & the sea as old. We are the last leaves on the tree, and one by one, like emigrants, we will take our leave of Morar. Our kind is going off the face of the earth.

('But you said you thoght you might live to be a hundred!' said I.)

No! This slow horse has allmost reached the mill. And since every enterprise that once I turned my mind to is now left behind, it is time for me to attend to my prayers and stand close to God.

Post Scriptum

Ten weeks after our latest meeting Ian died in his home at Brinacory. The date was 11th February 1794, and he was in his ninetieth year. Word of his decline had travelled quickly to Inverbeg and I was able to get to his bed side in time. He was awake, and he recognised me. We spoke a few words together; he knew that his death was near. I pray'd with him, and gave him the Viaticum, and shortly afterwards he past away, with his family round him.

Second Postscript

My intention of giving these memoirs to the interested public has never yet been accomplished, and I fear it will not be now. They have lain above forty-five years in my house.

During all that time I have been among the people of North Morar: if I am spared for three more I will be sixty years their priest. For sure, I am no longer the young 'prentice here who first made Ian's acquaintance. Indeed, I should myself be tempted to pen the further memorials of this people – that is, of his own descendants and their neighbours – were not skill and strength wanting.

In the New World beyond the ocean our countrymen have thrived and prospered. Betimes we get news of them. The country wherein they settled is now named 'Glengarry', after their former homeland, and year by year they tame a portion more of its great forests. Most pass their days and raise their families in quiet obscurity. I believe Ian's grand-daughter Anna is living yet, with grandchildren of her own.

Here at home it is twenty-five years or more since the road was made that now runs from Loch nan Ceall to Fort William – the town that Ian called 'Garrison' – and because of it we enjoy a little more intercourse with the outside world, and hear more of the English tongue. The old road above the head of our loch lies overgrown and hardly to be seen, for we now make use of the new one to reach Inverness town or the Low Country, first travelling West to the place at the coast where it begins, before we journey East upon it: so a part of what Michaelina foretold is already come to pass.

There were Morar men in the digging of the road; and others who laboured in Lochaber on the Great Canal; and they all returned home with silver in their purse. We had a few years of Plenty at that time, one way or another. The war against the French brought the price for cattle to the highest that it has ever been, and in like wise the price for kelp. But once it ended they soon fell again, and in most years since then our people have struggled to live. Lately the droves are diminished, and we never now see the kelp burners at their work, but only their huts by the shore abandoned.

If four families lived on one farm when I came first to this country, now the same land is shared by seven. Some are destitute. Through the scarcity of corn we have learned to count ever more on the potato for our daily food. But thrice in the past seven years the crop has been wasted with the blight, to our people's great distress. In those years one or two were even seen to beg, a sight hitherto unknown in North Morar. Should it ever fail entirely, many would surely starve.

Yet we have much to thank God for. We have good health whenever food is plentiful. And that disease, the Smallpox, is almost disappeared from our country now, which Ian and his generation held in such fear that they would not speak its name.

Here the Faith grows strong again in the sweet air of freedom. Just seven years ago we built a fine new church above the loch at Bracorina, and it is our great pride. The first infant to be baptised in its font was John Angus, the youngest son of that same little Donald who was in Ian's company on the day he talked to me of the changing times, and of his hopes and fears for the future.

If I look into that future, I dare say there will be good days and bad for us, and other and different trials. And I pray that men then will be as stead-fast and generous in freedom as the people of Ian's day were in adversity. We have much for which to thank them. May God be merciful to them, and to us all!

Bracorina, on the Feast of St Michael,
29th September, 1839.

Notes

1   'Ian mac Ian Roy vich Yonill' – Ian, son of red headed
      Ian, son of Donald. The translator has already named
      Ian in the English manner, but adds his Gaelic name,
      since this is how he would be known. In the Gaelic
      manner of naming there are no 'surnames' in the Eng-
      lish sense, but a first name followed by a patronymic or
      some other identifier. The translator's Gaelic spelling
      is typical of that found in 18th Century English texts,
      and is a very rough rendering of the Gaelic sounds. In
      correct Gaelic spelling it would be written Iain mac
      Iain Ruaidh mhic Dhomhnaill.

6   In the old Highland way the everyday world was full
      of signs, some good, some bad. To see a cuckoo on
      one's roof, especially before taking food in the morn-
      ing, was considered by many a sure sign of an immi-
      nent death.

7   'Glengarry's Morar' – i.e. North Morar, the district
      that lies between Loch Morar and Loch Nevis, being
      part of the lands of Glengarry. In the same way South
      Morar, the area south of the loch, is referred to as
      'Morar's Morar', being the main part of the lands of
      MacDonald of Morar.

11   It is said that the potato was introduced into Uist in
      1743, and probably brought from there to the Inner
      Isles and the Western Highlands from the 1750s.

12   The Beatons were the main hereditary medical family
      of the medieval Highlands and Islands, the dynasty
      lasting from the eleventh to the eighteenth century.
      For a number of generations they were Physicians to
      the Court of Scotland, and to the Lords of the Isles.
      The last documentary evidence for a member of the

family practising in Knoydart is for Aeneas (Angus) Beaton in 1718.

13   Feast of St Michael, or Michaelmass – 29 September.

13   The Stone at Tarbert – without churches after the Reformation, the Catholics of the Highlands celebrated Mass wherever they could. This often meant outdoors, using a large flat boulder as an altar. Several such Mass Stones have been identified in the Highlands.

18   Ian hoped that it was past midnight because Friday was considered an unlucky day. Similarly, one was considered safer from the supernatural if standing below high water mark, and if surrounded by a circle marked out on the ground.

18   Perhaps the last sighting and killing of a wolf in Scotland was by the Findhorn river in 1743, though there are a number of 'last sightings' claimed, in Glen Affric, Glen Roy and elsewhere. The original meaning of Eilean Allmha, the island in Loch Morar quite close to the mouth of the Meoble river, was 'Wolf Island'.

35   1 Merk = £⅔ Scots. £12 Scots = £1 Sterling. Thus £1 Scots = 1s. 8d. Sterling, 1 Merk = 1s. 1⅓d. Sterling. The reward of 500 Merks was thus worth £27 15s. 6 ⅔d.

38   'Arasaid' – the Arisaid was a traditional dress of Highland women, and was already going out of use by the early eighteenth century. A cloak reaching to the heels, belted at the waist and fastened at the breast, it was made of undyed wool woven with several stripes.

39   Scalan farm was situated in the Braes of Glenlivet, (Ord. Survey grid ref. 246194), about five miles ENE

of the present-day village of Tomintoul. Opened as a seminary to replace Eilean Bàn ('The White Island') in 1716, it remained in use until 1799, when the seminary was removed to Aquhorties, Aberdeenshire. Raided in 1728, and partly destroyed after Culloden, it was repaired and re-opened the following year, and completely rebuilt in stone in 1767. It acted as seminary for all Scotland between 1716 and 1732, in which year the seminary on Eilean Bàn was re-opened to train priests for the Highland District (cf. p. 74), whereafter Scalan served the same purpose for the Lowland District.

44   The lead mine opened near Strontian in 1724, under a partnership which included Sir Alex. Murray, the new owner of the estate of Ardnamurchan and Sunnart. Having run at a loss it was leased in 1730 to the York Building Company, who extended and developed it. Its financial difficulties continued, however, and after industrial disputes the mine was closed in 1740. It was later re-opened, and continued in operation until about 1815.

51   Alexander MacDonald (Alasdair mac Mhaighstir Alasdair), perhaps the greatest of all Gaelic poets, was born c. 1698, and died c. 1770. His father was Episcopalian minister of Islandfinnan. In 1729 Alexander was appointed master of the school for Islandfinnan by the SSPCK, and catechist for the parish of Ardnamurchan. He taught at the school until 1732, when he became the school master at Kilmory and, after several further changes, at Corryvullin, remaining there until dismissed in July 1745, just days before the landing of Charles Edward Stuart (cf. p. 91).

52   The verses are from Alexander's poem *Cuachag an Thasaich*.

54   A crusie lamp was an oil burning lamp with a bowl

(often made from a knot of wood) to hold the oil, and a wick. Fish oil was usually used in the coastal areas.

55 'Black meall' (blackmail) was money paid by strangers in exchange for protection by the local chieftain while passing through his land.

55 The river close by Lochiel's house is the Arkaig; the wider river is the Lochy.

56 'On most we put four shoes, but on some ... we put eight' – these were half shoes, worn either two to a hoof (i.e. eight in all), or only on the outer hoof (i.e. four in all).

58 230 shillings Scots was equivalent to 19s. 2d. Sterling.

59 Rannoch Moor was notorious at the time for robbers, and was avoided by travellers where possible.

67 In some parts of the Highlands it was customary for the groom to attend the wedding with his left shoe untied, for good luck's sake.

67 'The drones were like twin lambs . . .' – in parts of the Western Highlands, probably including North Morar, bagpipes had only two (tenor) drones at this time.

68 If an activity involved movement in a circle this was always done *deiseal* or sunwise. It would have been considered propitious to walk thus round a house before occupying it. It would have been especially appropriate to do this three times, three being a fortunate number, the number of the Trinity.

68 It was the custom, after a woman was married, for the snood (the headwear of an unmarried girl) to be replaced by the kerch which signified the married state.

71   'One quarter Boll of oats' – in the Trone measure, used for weighing grain and meal, 1 Boll = 16 Pecks = 96 Pints. There was, however, a great deal of local variation as to the values of such measures.

71   All Saints' Day – 1 November.

75   'The Sickness' – i.e. the Smallpox. This disease was the greatest cause of infant mortality at the time, and so prevalent and feared that people would not refer to it by name.

76   A Tacksman was one who in the clan system held land in tack (rent) directly from the Chief, and himself in turn rented parts of it to tenants. He had the status of Gentleman, next in seniority to the Chief.

83   There is doubt as to exactly where in Glenfinnan Prince Charlie raised the Standard. It may well have been on the flat land beside the loch where the monument now stands, which was suitable for a large gathering but boggy, or on higher ground where the party could be seen by clansmen arriving from the East, West and South. I have chosen the latter location.

84   The Battle of Killiecrankie, 1689, in which the Jacobite army under Bonnie Dundee defeated the Government forces of General Mackay. The Battle of Sheriffmuir (to which Iain also refers in Chap. 2) was fought in 1715 between the Jacobites under the Earl of Mar and the Government army led by the Duke of Argyll. It ended with both sides claiming victory.

85   It was customary for unbaptised infants to be buried quietly by the family some distance from the house.

93   McHimmie – (i.e. 'the son of Simon' in Gaelic) Lord Lovat.

100   The Prince's 'last house' before the hideout in Meoble was
      a narrow cave close by the shore of Loch nan Uamh.
      Betty Burke was of course the name that he himself
      adopted when travelling disguised as Flora MacDon-
      ald's maidservant.

105   The MacCrimmons were the hereditary pipers to
      MacLeod of Skye and for years had a celebrated school
      of piping at Boreraig. Among the dynasty's best known
      members were Domhnall Mór, who composed a great
      number of tunes in the early seventeenth century,
      including 'MacDonell of Glengarry'; Pádruig Mór,
      who ran the school in the second half of the century
      and was the composer of 'I gave a kiss to the king's
      hand' on the occasion of his meeting Charles II; and
      his son Pádruig Og, a composer of merit though noted
      more for his masterly playing, who flourished in the
      early eighteenth century.

106   Alexander Campbell of Doune was a noted gunsmith
      at this time. Some of the finest pistols, often beauti-
      fully engraved and inlaid, were made in the villages of
      Doune and Muthill.

107   'That old otter skin' – the skin of the otter was a
      favoured covering for a targe, being considered a par-
      ticularly effective protection.

114   William Roy's map, the fruit of his survey begun c.
      1748 and left incomplete in 1755 owing to the immi-
      nence of war, is now held in the British Museum. A
      set of photographic slides of the original is available
      for consultation in the Map Library of the National
      Library of Scotland. Roy was employed by the Post
      Office in Edinburgh at the time. He joined the Army
      in 1755 and in time rose to the rank of General. His
      survey of the districts around Lochs Morar and Nevis
      could not have been made later than the summer of
      1751.

116   The verse 'And should you come again ... ' is from *Òran Luaidh No Fùcaidh*, a Jacobite poem written in the guise of a love song to a sweetheart who has gone over the water.

117   Bishop Hugh MacDonald used the aliases McAlister, Sandison, McKay, and Scott at various times of his life. He also on occasion referred to himself as McKenzie.

118   Extant letters from this period include sections written in Italian and Latin, as well as examples of code words and aliases.

122   The Sgurr of Eigg – the steep sided, curiously shaped peak at the southern end of Eigg, which is the highest point on the island and gives it its distinctive appearance.

123   *Ite Missa Est* – the concluding words of dismissal of the Mass in Latin.

125   'The War against the ffrench' – i.e. Seven Years War (1756–63).

125   The church at Inverbeg remains to this day as a ruin. For years, after it had been abandoned, it was used as a sheep fank. The present description of the building of it is based on a survey made by the author. Though the exact date of building is not known the church certainly dates from Penal times.

127   'They did it to get back their land' – their land having been forfeited to the Crown after the '45.

130   75 Merks = £50 Scots = £4 3s. 4d. Sterling.

131   It was thought that every shoal of herring was led by a King.

132   Buss – the name given to a large, sea-going fishing
       vessel. Most of these were based on the Clyde, from
       where they annually sailed to the sea lochs of the
       Western Highlands. Easily the most popular sea loch
       for fishing, because the most prolific in herring, was
       Loch Hourn 'on the far side of Knoidart'.

136   There was at the time a flourishing trade in smuggled
       liquor, as well as smuggled salt.

138   Alexander's verse, and his description of himself as
       helmsman, are quotations from the storm episode of
       his own most famous poem *Birlinn Chlann Ràghnaill*
       (The Galley of Clanranald). The poem opens with the
       line 'God bless the barge of Clanranald!'

138   'The Seal was an other fish … ' – Martin Martin,
       writing at the end of the seventeenth century, tells of a
       debate between two islanders as to whether seal meat
       might be eaten in Lent, the argument in favour being
       that the seal is in fact a species of fish.

139   Kerban – i.e. Basking shark.

142   'The Island Across' – Highland and Island fishermen
       habitually used 'Noa terms' for places reached by sea,
       rather than use the correct names which, they believed,
       could bring misfortune, 'The Island Across' was the
       name used for Canna.

142   The new houses given to 'foreigners' – i.e. to persons
       from furth of the lands of Glengarry.

144   Fulling (or 'waulking' as it is more often called today)
       was the process of stretching cloth after it was woven,
       so that it would retain its shape and size thereafter.
       The fulling was undertaken by a group of perhaps a
       dozen women, sitting on two sides of a board or table,

working as a team, and co-ordinating their actions by the singing of rhythmic songs.

164   'The war against the ffrench' – i.e. the Seven Years War (1756–63); the 'fight against the American rebels' refers to the American War of Independence (1775–83).

167   These lines are from the poem *O Siud an Taobh a Ghabhainn* by Anna Gillies of Morar, written about a year before her emigration to America from Knoydart in 1786. I have made Ian's grand-daughter Anna the same person as this poetess; she would be a Gillies as the daughter of Ian's own daughter Mary (McLellan) and Calum Ian (Gillies). And since Anna married Ronald MacDonald of Knoydart, their son Ian Bàn and the rest of their children would be MacDonalds.

167   60 Merks = £40 Scots = £3 6s. 8d. Sterling.

170   'The Island of the Forest' is Rum (cf. the note to p. 142).

St Brigid's feast – 1 February.

179   Garrison – i.e. Fort William (in Gaelic *An Gearasdan*).

180   Cas Chrom (lit. 'bent foot') – an angled spade used for turning the soil in terrain too rough and uneven for the plough. It had a long handle, and a blade set at an angle and shaped rather like a pointed foot. Near to the joint of handle and blade was a pin, by which the blade was driven into the earth with the foot.

181   'At war with the ffrench again' – i.e. the French Revolutionary Wars of 1793–1802.

187   'The gift of the Two Sights' – i.e. Second Sight.

188   Michaelina's predictions have all come about. The clue to her prediction of sheep rubbing their flanks against the altar of Inverbeg can be found in the note to p. 125. The solution to her prediction that the people would travel West in order to go East will be found in the story on p. 192. The other predictions the reader is left to work out for him/herself!

    'As old as a Hebridean' – the people of the Hebrides were reputedly very long lived.

189   Viaticum ('food for the journey') – the Eucharist given to the dying,

192   'The Great Canal' – the Caledonian Canal, built under the direction of Thomas Telford. By linking the lochs of the Great Glen, the canal provided a waterway from the North Sea to the West. Digging commenced in 1803, with teams working simultaneously from the Eastern and Western ends, and was completed in 1821. It was in the team at the Western (Lochaber) end that Morar men were employed.

    In fact the potato crop was to fail in successive years from 1846, causing a devastating famine in the Highlands. The tragedy is less well remembered than it should be, overshadowed as it was by the greater horror of the Irish potato famine of the same years.

Eilein na h-Òige
The Poems of Fr Allan McDonald,
ed. Ronald Black
ISBN: 1-901157-61-X

The name of Fr Allan McDonald (Maighstir Ailein, 1859-1905) is evergreen in the Gaelic-speaking islands of Uist, Barra and Eriskay. A native of Fort William, he wore himself out in the service of his parishioners at Dailburgh, and was transferred in 1894 to Eriskay, his beloved Eilein na h-Òige: 'Isle of Youth'. Among his labours was the publication of a Gaelic hymnal which Ronald Black, the editor, has combined selections of in this volume with twenty-seven poems first published in 1965, providing a resulting body of some sixty items with an English translation, introduction and notes.

Ronald Black is Gaelic editor of The Scotsman and the Uist newspaper Am Pàipear. He has published *An Tuil: Anthology of 20th Century Scottish Gaelic Verse* (1999), *Smuaintean fo Éiseabhal* (2000) the poetry of Dòmhnall Aonghais Bhàin of South Uist and *An Lasair: Anthology of 18th Century Scottish Gaelic Verse* (2001).

Mungo Books is an imprint of Ovada Books devoted to publications of Scottish Catholic interest.

Ovada Books, an activity of the Passionists in Scotland and Ireland, has as its aims the promotion of Catholic faith and culture; supporting the ministry of the Passionists; and helping people to understand the Catholic Faith through publishing, retailing and other means.

If you would like further information on how you can help our work, please contact us at

Ovada Books
St Mungo's Retreat
52 Parson Street
Glasgow
G4 0RX

+44 (0)141 552 5523

Scottish Charity Number SCO 15760
The Passionist Fathers